MODERN LONGMAN LITERATURE

Ten D H Lawrence Short Stories

Selected and edited by
Andrew Whittle and Roy Blatchford

Contents

The writer on writing

D H Lawrence is probably best known as a novelist, although he was also a poet, a playwright, a literary critic and a painter. In addition, he wrote over fifty short stories, sketches and novellas (a kind of short novel). His output, during his short life, was immense and he is one of the most important and controversial literary figures in the development of early twentieth-century English literature. He refused to conform and much of his work was socially and sexually too outspoken for its time, which led to some of his titles being banned.

He warned readers to be careful when reading a story:

> *a great deal of the meaning of life and of art lies in the apparently dull places, the pauses, the unimportant passages.*

In many ways his short stories are straightforward but to appreciate the messages and ideas you must read them carefully. Lawrence was the first great writer to tell the reader: 'Never trust the story-teller, trust the tale.'

Here Lawrence is reminding you of the importance of personal reaction to his writing and the value of your ideas that are stimulated about the characters, the narrative, the atmosphere, the descriptions and the themes as you read.

The literary critic Philip Hobsbaum described the most important features of Lawrence's early short stories:

> *the reader is intensely aware of the seeing eye, the sense of nature, and, more, the keen ear for language.*

In many ways this sums up what Lawrence was trying to do in many of his short stories.

- Lawrence wanted to explain the way he *noticed* people and the way they behave.
- Lawrence wanted to *show* how the natural environment and people's animal instincts unconsciously affect the way they live.
- He wanted to *describe* the interesting and revealing ways people talk and unfold their hidden feelings.

Lawrence felt that all too often these basic aspects of our lives were invisible in our everyday world. As he said in a letter to a friend: 'The visible world is not true. The invisible world is true and real.'

Introduction

The writer's background

David Herbert Lawrence was born on 11 September 1885 in the reign of Queen Victoria. He grew up at a time when Britain was a strong colonial and economic power with influence all over the world. The family, however, was very poor and lived in the Nottinghamshire mining town of Eastwood. David was the fourth of five children. As he grew up, he saw a contrast between the quiet local countryside and the industrial world of hard, dirty and dangerous physical labour.

Lawrence began to hate the drudgery and insecurity working people had to suffer in Britain at that time. His father, Arthur, could not really read or write and was sometimes brutal towards his family. In contrast, Lawrence's mother, Lydia, was a bright woman, who had been a teacher and was often forceful as she tried to better the lives of her children.

Lawrence was a quick learner and won a scholarship to Nottingham High School which he attended from 1898 to 1901 when he became very ill with pneumonia and was nursed by his devoted mother. After a short time as a clerk in a factory, he became a student-teacher in a local school. In 1906 he started his studies at Nottingham University College. While at university he met a local girl, Jessie Chambers, and they quickly struck up a very important and close friendship which lasted until 1911. At this time Lawrence published his first novel ***The White Peacock***.

From 1908 to 1911 Lawrence was employed as a teacher in Croydon. He hated it and became ill, which allowed him time for writing. In 1912 Lawrence met his great love, Frieda Weekley. For most people living in Britain, during the period before World War I

(1914–1918), Lawrence's affair with the married Frieda was unacceptable and a social taboo, especially as she had children. They eloped to Europe and, after her divorce, they were married in 1914.

Sons and Lovers, Lawrence's second novel, appeared in 1913. It was mostly autobiographical and rather falsely portrayed Jessie as the character Miriam. ***The Rainbow*** was published in 1915 but was banned because of its openness about sex and relationships. At this time most people thought that writing about sex was obscene and others still thought that women were second-class citizens. Lawrence supported the slow changes in the role of woman in society. World War I brought women new-found freedoms as they took over the jobs of men who were away at the Front, and after 1918 the place of women in society gradually improved.

After leaving Britain in 1919, the Lawrences spent most of their unconventional and emotionally stormy lives travelling in Europe, USA, Mexico, Australia, New Zealand and Sri Lanka. The novel ***Women in Love*** appeared in 1920, followed by ***Aaron's Rod*** (1922), ***Kangaroo*** (1923) and ***The Plumed Serpent*** (1926). ***Lady Chatterley's Love***r was privately printed in Italy in 1928. (It could not be published in full in England until 1960.) The couple eventually returned to live in Europe, but on 2 March 1930 Lawrence died from tuberculosis at the early age of 44.

Ten D H Lawrence stories

Adolf and ***Rex*** are companion tales which retell childhood memories in a simple and entertaining way. Lawrence wrote them in 1919 and 1920. ***A Prelude***, a story full of rural detail, was written in 1907 and won the *Nottinghamshire Guardian* short story prize. Lawrence cheated and submitted three pieces: ***A Prelude*** was submitted under the name of Jessie Chambers.

Lessford's Rabbits and ***A Lesson on a Tortoise*** are sketches written while Lawrence was a teacher in Croydon. They show deep frustration with his work and his dismay at the lives of his pupils. In 1910, while still a teacher, he broke off his long engagement with Jessie Chambers and then was briefly engaged to another local Nottinghamshire girl, Louie Burrows. ***The Shades of Spring*** and ***Second Best*** are about strong-willed women making choices between lovers and both date from this time in Lawrence's life.

Her Turn, written in 1912, is also about a clash between a man and a woman. It is set in Nottinghamshire during the National Coal Miners' Strike of the same year. In ***Tickets, Please***, written in 1915 and set in Nottingham, Lawrence tells a story of women taking revenge on an arrogant man and returns to the theme of conflict between men and women. ***The Lovely Lady***, written in the 1920s, has a supernatural feel and is the story of two women: a dominant mother who finally accepts that her son must marry and a young woman who makes sure she gets the man she wants.

Plot

The simple but carefully constructed plots of Lawrence's stories help the reader appreciate his point of view. Many of his stories are intentionally open-ended so you are left to make up your own mind. The stories written in the third person such as ***Her Turn*** or ***The Lovely Lady*** build up the suspense precisely until the very end of the tale.

Characters

Lawrence's descriptions of people are often very detailed and how a person looks can give an insight into personality. For example, in ***A Prelude*** the brothers are finely drawn and have different physical characteristics which help you to understand them. In ***The Lovely***

Lady the mother is compared with various strong, beautiful women from the past and so the reader realises her power and obsession.

Setting

One of the most distinctive features of Lawrence's short stories in this collection is his use of description to create mood. For example, vivid pieces of descriptive storytelling set the tone and atmosphere in ***The Shades of Spring*** as Syson walks through the fields. Later Hilda shows him the real beauty of the countryside, something he has forgotten because of his city life. In this story and others such as ***Adolf*** or ***Second Best*** Lawrence describes the beautiful countryside he felt people usually ignore in their busy lives.

Lawrence's descriptions and settings are often full of realism and he tries to show life in an unsentimental way. For example in ***A Prelude*** the picture of the kitchen has detail that emphasises the simple values and life of the family.

Style

Adolf, ***Rex***, ***A Lesson on a Tortoise*** and ***Lessford's Rabbits*** are all written in the first person and draw the reader into Lawrence's world, so helping you understand his joys and frustrations as the stories unfold.

Lawrence's images are very carefully chosen and often repeated to suggest atmosphere and to reinforce ideas and symbolism. For example, the blind mole in ***Second Best*** makes the reader realise how blind and lost humans can be when searching for love. Frances kills the mole and this act symbolises the end of her love for Jimmy. The imagery of touch in ***Tickets, Please*** evokes the power of sensual body contact.

Themes

Lawrence's short stories are dominated by his own, sometimes unconventional ideas about life. The themes in these tales are interwoven as Lawrence returns time and time again to the same issues and explores his own concerns about the world around him. Lawrence came into contact with many of the intellectuals and thinkers of his time. He used some of their ideas to form his own rather individual thoughts about life. For example, he was very influenced by the theories of Sigmund Freud who studied the unconscious thoughts of people and how experiences in childhood can affect adults later in life.

Animals and nature

Lawrence was intrigued by the untamed ways of animals and nature. ***Adolf*** and ***Rex*** have animals at the centre of the stories, but in both, the humans fail to break the wildness in the creatures. In ***Second Best*** and ***Her Turn*** the humans are compared to the creatures in the story or given animal characteristics. The reptile in ***A Lesson on a Tortoise*** keeps calm despite the anarchy in the classroom, and this time it is the boys who are wild.

Lessford's Rabbits describes a boy's care and concern for his animals, while the description of the countryside in ***The Shades of Spring*** shows Lawrence's knowledge and appreciation of nature.

Family and mothers

Several of these stories also show Lawrence's preoccupation with families (in particular, mothers) and conflict between parents. In ***Adolf*** and ***Rex*** the narrators suggest the differences between the mother and the father, which contrasts with the idyllic portrayal of the family in ***The Shades of Spring***. In ***A Prelude*** the mother is concerned about her sons while in ***Her Turn*** the parents are caught up in conflict. In the later tale ***The Lovely Lady*** the bond between mother and son has gone badly wrong.

Men, women and relationships

Lawrence's fiction is dominated by his interest in the relationships between men and women and the psychological impulses that make people behave the way they do. He saw people as being continually wrapped up in small but important conflicts with each other.

Love and the struggle between Lawrence's male and female characters are major themes in all Lawrence's writing and feature strongly in this collection. Many of the tales are based on emotional triangles where ex-lovers, potential lovers or current lovers seem to be locked in conflict. Quite often there seems to be a lot of misunderstanding between the sexes; sometimes, as in ***Second Best***, the woman is very independent but is strongly attracted to a man who is not quite suitable. In ***Tickets, Please*** the women have pride in their jobs and are understandably outraged at the promiscuous John Thomas. They take their revenge but the reader is left unsure who really wins the battle between the man and the women.

Social class and status

Lawrence hated the class system of his time and all that it stood for. The early story ***A Prelude*** shows social status getting in the way of true love. In the last story of this collection, ***The Lovely Lady***, Ciss, a poor cousin, is left in little doubt that Mrs Attenborough does not see her as a suitable daughter-in-law. In most cases Lawrence thought that love and physical attraction could overcome the class divisions which threatened to keep people apart.

The human spirit

Lawrence was very concerned with the dignity of people. He felt that all human beings were essentially equal but they were confused by modern life which seems to be dominated by work, money and the media. As far as he was concerned most people had lost their links with Nature. In ***The Shades of Spring*** Syson is alienated from the countryside he once knew. At the end of ***Second Best***, Frances appears to be emotionally crushed because she has to make a confusing decision between two types of men.

Compulsion and destiny

Lawrence's short stories often try to explore the unconscious forces that control people's behaviour. Some of the characters in these tales are not in control of their destinies. Often the young men and women in the stories cannot relate to each other but somehow are forced together. The lovers in ***Second Best*** are confused by how their minds tell them to behave and what their emotions make them do. In contrast, Hilda in ***The Shades of Spring*** makes a positive decision about her life and rejects Syson for the passionate Arthur, while Ciss takes control of her destiny in ***The Lovely Lady***, but is still shocked by what happens.

Reading log

The study programme at the back of this book provides many ideas and activities for *after* you have read the short stories. However, you are likely to give a better response to the text if you make some notes *as* you read. Those who assess your coursework assignments or examination answers are looking for evidence of a personal response to literature; to do well, this should be supported by some close analysis and reference to detail.

Keeping notes as you read should help you to provide this, as well as to keep track of events in the plot, characters and relationships and the time-scheme of the stories. When you are reading, stop every so often and use the following prompt questions and suggestions to note down key points and details.

Plot

- What have been the main developments in the plot? Note down exactly where they occur.
- How has the author 'moved the story on' – for example, by introducing a new character or by a change of setting?
- Is there more than one storyline?
- How do you expect the plot/s to develop? As you read on, consider whether you predicted accurately or whether there have been some surprises.

Characters

- What are your initial impressions of the main characters? Are these impressions confirmed or altered as you read? How?

- Do any of the main characters change or develop through a story? How and why?
- How are you responding to individual characters? In particular, are you aware that you are identifying or sympathising with one of them? Are you conscious of ways in which the author is making or encouraging you to do this, for example by focusing on his/her point of view, or by providing insights into his/her thoughts and feelings?

Setting

The setting of a story is the place and time in which the events happen. Sometimes the setting involves a particular community or culture. It can often make an important contribution to the prevailing atmosphere of the story.

- How well does the writer help you to visualise the setting? Make a note of any passages of description which you think are particularly effective in creating a vivid sense of place and time.
- Does the setting seem to be just a background against which the action takes place, for example because it is concerned with historical events or with the interrelationship between people and their environment?

Themes

The themes of a work of literature are the *broad* ideas or aspects of experiences which it is about. There are some themes – love, death, war, politics, religion, the environment – which writers have explored throughout the centuries.

- What theme or themes seem to be emerging in each story?
- How is the theme developed? For example, do different characters represent different attitudes or beliefs?

- Does it seem that the writer wants to express his/her attitude to a theme, to raise questions, or just to make the reader reflect on it?

Style

- Is the story told by a narrator who is also a character in the story, referring to him/herself as 'I' (first-person narrative), or is the narrator anonymous and detached from the action (third-person narrative)?
- How does this affect the story? For example, does a third-person narrator tell you what characters are thinking and feeling (known as an *omniscient* narrator) or comment directly on characters and/or events?
- Note down any interesting or striking use of language, such as powerful words and images which evoke a sense of atmosphere. Include any recurring or similar images.
- What do you think of the dialogue? Do the 'voices' of the characters sound real and convincing? Make a note of any particular features of the language used in the dialogue, such as dialect, colloquialisms, slang or expletives (swearing).
- How is the dialogue used, for example to show characters and relationships, for humour, to explore theme?

Your personal response

- How are your feelings about the collection developing as you read? What have you enjoyed or admired most (or least) and why?
- Has the collection made you think about or influenced your views on its theme/s?

Ten D H Lawrence Short Stories

Adolf

When we were children our father often worked on the night-shift. Once it was spring-time, and he used to arrive home, black and tired, just as we were downstairs in our nightdresses. Then night met morning face to face, and the contact was not always happy. Perhaps it was painful to my father to see us gaily entering upon the day into which he dragged himself soiled and weary. He didn't like going to bed in the spring morning sunshine.

But sometimes he was happy, because of his long walk through the dewy fields in the first daybreak. He loved the open morning, the crystal and the space, after a night down pit. He watched every bird, every stir in the trembling grass, answered the whinnying of the peewits and tweeted to the wrens. If he could, he also would have whinnied and tweeted and whistled in a native language that wasn't human. He liked non-human things best.

One sunny morning we were all sitting at table when we heard his heavy slurring walk up the entry. We became uneasy. His was always a disturbing presence, trammelling. He passed the window darkly, and we heard him go into the scullery and put down his tin bottle. But directly he came into the kitchen we felt at once that he had something to communicate. No one spoke. We watched his black face for a second.

'Give me a drink,' he said.

My mother hastily poured out his tea. He went to pour it out into his saucer. But instead of drinking it he suddenly put something on the table among the tea-cups. A tiny brown rabbit! A small rabbit, a mere morsel, sitting against the bread as still as if it were a made thing.

'A rabbit! a young one! Who gave it to you, Father?'

But he laughed, enigmatically, with a sliding motion of his

yellow-gray eyes, and went to take off his coat. We pounced on the rabbit.

'Is it alive? Can you feel its heart beat?'

My father came back and sat down heavily in his armchair. He dragged his saucer to him, and blew his tea, pushing out his red lips under his black moustache.

'Where did you get it, Father?'

'I picked it up,' he said, wiping his fore-arm over his mouth and beard.

'Where?'

'It's a wild one!' came my mother's quick voice.

'Yes, it is.'

'Then why did you bring it?' cried my mother.

'Oh, we wanted it,' came our cry.

'Yes, I've no doubt you did,' retorted my mother. But she was drowned in our clamour of questions. On the field-path my father had found a dead mother rabbit and three dead little ones – this one alive, but unmoving.

'But what had killed them, Daddy?'

'I couldn't say, my child. I s'd think she'd aten something.'

'Why did you bring it!' again my mother's voice of condemnation. 'You know what it will be.'

My father made no answer, but we were loud in protest.

'He must bring it. It's not big enough to live by itself.'

'It would die,' we shouted.

'Yes, and it will die now. And then there'll be another outcry.'

My mother set her face against the tragedy of dead pets. Our hearts sank.

'It won't die, Father, will it? Why will it? It won't.'

'I s'd think not,' said my father.

'You know well enough it will. Haven't we had it all before!' said my mother.

'They dunna always pine,' replied my father testily.

But my mother reminded him of other little wild animals he had brought, which had sulked and refused to live, and brought storms of tears and trouble in our house of lunatics. Trouble fell on us. The little rabbit sat on our lap, unmoving, its eyes wide and dark. We brought it milk, warm milk, and held it to its nose. It sat as still as if it was far away, retreated down some deep burrow, hidden, oblivious. We wetted its mouth and whiskers with drops of milk. It gave no sign, did not even shake off the wet, white drops. Somebody began to shed a few secret tears.

'What did I say?' cried my mother. 'Take it and put it down in the field.'

Her command was in vain. We were driven to get dressed for school. There sat the rabbit. It was like a tiny obscure cloud. Watching it, the emotions died out of the breast. Useless to love it, to yearn over it. Its little feelings were all ambushed. They must be circumvented. Love and affection were a trespass upon it. A little wild thing, it became more mute and asphyxiated still in its own arrest, when we approached with love. We must not love it. We must circumvent it, for its own existence.

So I passed the order to my sister and mother. The rabbit was not to be spoken to, or even looked at. Wrapping it in a piece of flannel, I put it in an obscure corner of the cold parlour, and put a saucer of milk before its nose. My mother was forbidden to enter the parlour while we were at school.

'As if I should take any notice of your nonsense,' she cried, affronted. Yet I doubt if she ventured into the parlour.

At midday, after school, creeping into the front room, there we saw the rabbit still and unmoving in the piece of flannel. Strange grey-brown neutralisation of life, still living! It was a sore problem to us.

'Why won't it drink its milk, Mother?' we whispered. Our father was asleep.

'It prefers to sulk its life away, silly little thing.'

A profound problem. Prefers to sulk its life away!

We put young dandelion leaves to its nose. The sphinx was not more oblivious. Yet its eye was bright.

At teatime, however, it had hopped a few inches, out of its flannel, and there it sat again, uncovered, a little solid cloud of muteness with unmoving whiskers. Only its side palpitated slightly with life.

Darkness came. My father set out for work. The rabbit was still unmoving. Dumb despair was coming over the sisters, a threat of tears before bedtime. Clouds of my mother's anger gathered as she muttered against my father's wantonness.

Once more the rabbit was wrapped in the old pit-singlet. But now it was carried into the scullery and put under the copper fireplace, that it might imagine itself inside a burrow. The saucers were placed about, four or five, here and there on the floor, so that if the little creature should chance to hop abroad, it could not fail to come upon some food. After this my mother was allowed to take from the scullery what she wanted and then she was forbidden to open the door.

When morning came and it was light, I went downstairs. Opening the scullery door, I heard a slight scuffle. Then I saw dabbles of milk all over the floor and tiny rabbit-droppings in the saucers. And there was the miscreant, the tips of his ears showing behind a pair of boots. I peeped at him. He sat bright-eyed and askance, twitching his nose and looking at me while not looking at me.

He was alive – very much alive. But we were still afraid to trespass much on his confidence.

'Father!' My father was arrested at the door. 'Father, the rabbit's alive!'

'Back your life it is,' said my father.

'Mind how you go in.'

By evening, however, the little creature was tame, quite tame. He was christened Adolf. We were enchanted by him. We couldn't really love him, because he was wild and loveless to the end. But he was an unmixed delight.

We decided he was too small to live in a hutch – he must live at large in the house. My mother protested, but in vain. He was so tiny. So we had him upstairs, and he dropped tiny pills on the bed and we were enchanted.

Adolf made himself instantly at home. He had the run of the house and was perfectly happy, with his tunnels and his holes behind the furniture.

We loved him to take meals with us. He would sit on the table humping his back, sipping his milk, shaking his whiskers and his tender ears, hopping off and hobbling back to his saucer, with an air of supreme unconcern. Suddenly he was alert. He hobbled a few tiny paces, and reared himself up inquisitively at the sugar-basin. He fluttered his tiny forepaws, and then reached and laid them on the edge of the basin, whilst he craned his thin neck and peeped in. He trembled his whiskers at the sugar, then did his best to lift down a lump.

'*Do* you think I will have it! Animals in the sugar-pot!' cried my mother with a rap of her hand on the table.

Which so delighted the electric Adolf that he flung his hind-quarters and knocked over a cup.

'It's your own fault, Mother. If you left him alone –'

He continued to take tea with us. He rather liked warm tea. And he loved sugar. Having nibbled a lump, he would turn to the butter. There he was shoo'd off by our parent. He soon learned to treat her shooing with indifference. Still, she hated him to put his nose in the food. And he loved to do it. And one day between them they overturned the cream-jug. Adolf deluged his little chest, bounced back in terror, was seized by his little ears by my mother and bounced down on the hearth-rug. There he shivered in momentary discomfort, and suddenly set off in a wild flight to the parlour.

This last was his happy hunting-ground. He had cultivated the bad habit of pensively nibbling certain bits of cloth in the hearth-rug. When chased from this pasture, he would retreat under the sofa. There he would twinkle in meditation until suddenly, no one knew why, he would go off like an alarm clock. With a sudden bumping scuffle he would whirl out of the room, going through the doorway with his little ears flying.

Then we would hear his thunderbolt hurtling in the parlour, but before we could follow, the wild streak of Adolf would flash past us, on an electric wind that swept him round the scullery and carried him back, a little mad thing, flying possessed like a ball round the parlour. After which ebullition he would sit in a corner composed and distant, twitching his whiskers in abstract meditation. And it was in vain we questioned him about his outbursts. He just went off like a gun, and was as calm after it as a gun that smokes placidly.

Alas! he grew up rapidly. It was almost impossible to keep him from the outer door.

One day, as we were playing by the stile, I saw his brown shadow loiter across the road and pass into the field that faced the houses. Instantly a cry of 'Adolf!' – a cry he knew full well. And instantly a wind swept him away down the sloping meadow, tail twinkling and zig-zagging through the grass. After him we pelted. It was a strange sight to see him, ears back, his little loins so powerful, flinging the world behind him. We ran ourselves out of breath, but we could not catch him. Then somebody headed him off, and he sat with sudden unconcern, twitching his nose under a bunch of nettles.

His wanderings cost him a shock. One Sunday morning my father had just been quarrelling with a pedlar, and we were hearing the aftermath indoors, when there came a sudden unearthly scream from the yard. We flew out; there sat Adolf cowering under a bench, whilst a great black-and-white cat glowered intently at him a few yards away. Sight not to be forgotten. Adolf rolling back his eyes and parting his strange muzzle in another scream, the cat stretching forward in slow elongation.

Ha! how we hated that cat! How we pursued him over the chapel wall and across the neighbours' gardens. Adolf was still only half-grown.

'Cats!' said my mother. 'Hideous detestable animals! Why do people harbour them?'

But Adolf was becoming too much for her. Suddenly to hear

him clumping downstairs when she was alone in the house was startling. And to keep him from the door impossible. Cats prowled outside. It was worse than having a child to look after. Yet we would not have him shut up. He became more lusty, more callous than ever. He was a strong kicker, and many a scratch on face and arms did we owe to him. But he brought his own doom on himself. The lace curtains in the parlour – my mother was rather proud of them – fell on the floor very full. One of Adolf's joys was to scuffle wildly through them as though through some foamy under-growth. He had already torn rents in them.

One day he entangled himself altogether. He kicked, he whirled round in a mad nebulous inferno. He screamed – and brought down the curtain-rod with a smash, right on the best beloved geranium just as my mother rushed in. She extricated him, but she never forgave him.

Even we understood that he must go. It was decided, after a long deliberation, that my father should carry him back to the wild woods. Once again he was stowed into the great pocket of the pit-jacket.

'Best pop him i' the pot,' said my father, who enjoyed raising the wind of indignation.

And so, next day, our father said that Adolf, set down on the edge of the coppice, had hopped away with utmost indifference, neither elated nor moved. We heard it and believed. But many, many were the heart-searchings. How would the other rabbits receive him? Would they smell his tameness, his humanised degradation, and rend him? My mother pooh-poohed the extravagant idea.

However, he was gone, and we were rather relieved. My father kept an eye open for him. He declared that several times passing the coppice in the early morning, he had seen Adolf peeping through the nettle-stalks. He had called him in an odd, high-voiced, cajoling fashion. But Adolf had not responded. Wildness gains so soon upon its creatures. And they become so contemptuous then of our tame presence. So it seemed to me. I myself would go to the edge of the coppice, and call softly. I myself would imagine bright eyes between the nettle-stalks, flash of a white scornful tail past the bracken. That insolent white tail, as Adolf turned his flank on us.

Rex

Since every family has its black sheep, it almost follows that every man must have a sooty uncle. Lucky if he hasn't two. However, it is only with my mother's brother that we are concerned. She had loved him dearly when he was a little blond boy. When he grew up black, she was always vowing she would never speak to him again. Yet when he put in an appearance, after years of absence, she invariably received him in a festive mood, and was even flirty with him.

He rolled up one day in a dog-cart, when I was a small boy. He was large and bullet-headed and blustering, and this time, sporty. Sometimes he was rather literary, sometimes coloured with business. But this time he was in checks, and was sporty. We viewed him from a distance.

The upshot was, would we rear a pup for him. Now my mother detested animals about the house. She could not bear the mix-up of human with animal life. Yet she consented to bring up the pup.

My uncle had taken a large, vulgar public-house in a large and vulgar town. It came to pass that I must fetch the pup. Strange for me, a member of the Band of Hope, to enter the big, noisy, smelly plate-glass and mahogany public-house. It was called The Good Omen. Strange to have my uncle towering over me in the passage, shouting 'Hello, Johnny, what d'yer want?' He didn't know me. Strange to think he was my mother's brother, and that he had his bouts when he read Browning aloud with emotion and éclat.

I was given tea in a narrow, uncomfortable sort of living-room, half kitchen. Curious that such a palatial pub should show such miserable private accommodations, but so it was. There was I, unhappy, and glad to escape with the soft fat pup. It was winter-time, and I wore a big-flapped black overcoat, half cloak. Under the cloak-sleeves I hid the puppy, who trembled. It was Saturday, and the train was crowded, and he whimpered under my coat. I sat in mortal fear of being hauled out for travelling without a dog-ticket. However, we arrived, and my torments were for nothing.

The others were wildly excited over the puppy. He was small and fat and white, with a brown-and-black head: a fox terrier. My father said he had a lemon head – some such mysterious technical phraseology. It wasn't lemon at all, but coloured like a field bee. And he had a black spot at the root of his spine.

It was Saturday night – bath-night. He crawled on the hearth-rug like a fat white teacup, and licked the bare toes that had just been bathed.

'He ought to be called Spot,' said one. But that was too ordinary. It was a great question, what to call him.

'Call him Rex – the King,' said my mother, looking down on the fat, animated little teacup, who was chewing my sister's little toe and making her squeal with joy and tickles. We took the name in all seriousness.

'Rex – the King!' We thought it was just right. Not for years did I realise that it was a sarcasm on my mother's part. She must have wasted some twenty years or more of irony on our incurable naïveté.

It wasn't a successful name, really. Because my father and all the people in the street failed completely to pronounce the monosyllable Rex. They all said Rax. And it always distressed me. It always suggested to me seaweed, and rack-and-ruin. Poor Rex!

We loved him dearly. The first night we woke to hear him weeping and whinnying in loneliness at the foot of the stairs. When it could be borne no more, I slipped down for him, and he slept under the sheets.

'I won't have that little beast in the beds. Beds are not for dogs,' declared my mother callously.

'He's as good as we are!' we cried, injured.

'Whether he is or not, he's not going in the beds.'

I think now, my mother scorned us for our lack of pride. We were a little *infra dig*, we children.

The second night, however, Rex wept the same and in the same way was comforted. The third night we heard our father plod downstairs, heard several slaps administered to the yelling, dismayed puppy, and heard the amiable, but to us heartless voice saying 'Shut it then! Shut thy noise, 'st hear? Stop in thy basket, stop there!'

'It's a shame!' we shouted, in muffled rebellion, from the sheets.

'I'll give you shame, if you don't hold your noise and go to sleep,' called our mother from her room. Whereupon we shed angry tears and went to sleep. But there was a tension.

'Such a houseful of idiots would make me detest the little beast, even if he was better than he is', said my mother.

But as a matter of fact, she did not detest Rexie at all. She only had to pretend to do so, to balance our adoration. And in truth, she did not care for close contact with animals. She was too fastidious. My father, however, would take on a real dog's voice, taking to the puppy: a funny, high, sing-song falsetto which he seemed to produce at the top of his head. ''S a pretty little dog! 's a pretty little doggy! – ay! – yes! – he is, yes! – Wag thy strunt, then! Wag thy strunt, Rexie! – Ha-ha! Nay, tha munna –' This last as the puppy, wild with excitement at the strange falsetto voice, licked my father's nostrils and bit my father's nose with his sharp little teeth.

''E makes blood come,' said my father.

'Serves you right for being so silly with him,' said my mother. It was odd to see her as she watched the man, my father, crouching and talking to the little dog and laughing strangely when the little creature bit his nose and toused his beard. What does a woman think of her husband at such a moment?

My mother amused herself over the names we called him.

'He's an angel – he's a little butterfly – Rexie, my sweet!'

'Sweet! A dirty little object!' interpolated my mother. She

and he had a feud from the first. Of course he chewed boots and worried our stockings and swallowed our garters. The moment we took off our stockings he would dart away with one, we after him. Then as he hung, growling vociferously, at one end of the stocking, we at the other, we would cry:

'Look at him, Mother! He'll make holes in it again.' Whereupon my mother darted at him and spanked him sharply.

'Let go, sir, you destructive little fiend.'

But he didn't let go. He began to growl with real rage, and hung on viciously. Mite as he was, he defied her with a manly fury. He did not hate her, nor she him. But they had one long battle with one another.

'I'll teach you, my Jockey! Do you think I'm going to spend my life darning after your destructive little teeth! I'll show you if I will!'

But Rexie only growled more viciously. They both became really angry, while we children expostulated earnestly with both. He would not let her take the stocking from him.

'You should tell him properly, Mother. He won't be driven,' we said.

'I'll drive him father than he bargains for. I'll drive him out of my sight for ever, that I will,' declared my mother, truly angry. He would put her into a real temper, with his tiny, growling defiance.

'He's sweet! A Rexie, a little Rexie!'

'A filthy little nuisance! Don't think I'll put up with him.'

And to tell the truth, he was dirty at first. How could he be otherwise, so young! But my mother hated him for it. And perhaps this was the real start of their hostility. For he lived in the house with us. He would wrinkle his nose and show his tiny dagger-teeth in fury when he was thwarted, and his growls of real battle-rage against my mother rejoiced us as much as they angered her. But at last she caught him *in flagrante*. She pounced on him, rubbed his nose in the mess, and flung him out into the yard. He yelped with shame and disgust and indignation. I shall never forget the sight of him as he rolled over, then tried to turn his head away from the disgust of his own muzzle, shaking his little snout with a sort of horror, and trying to sneeze it off. My sister gave a yell of despair, and dashed out with a rag and a pan of water, weeping wildly. She sat in the middle of the yard with the befouled puppy, and shedding bitter tears she wiped him and washed him clean. Loudly she reproached my mother. 'Look how much bigger you are than he is. It's a shame, it's a shame!'

'You ridiculous little lunatic, you've undone all the good it would do him, with your soft ways. Why is my life made a curse with animals! Haven't I enough as it is –'

There was a subdued tension afterwards. Rex was a little white chasm between us and our parent.

He became clean. But then another tragedy loomed. He must be docked. His floating puppy-tail must be docked short. This time my father was the enemy. My mother agreed with us that it was an unnecessary cruelty. But my father was adamant. 'The dog'll look a fool all his life, if he's not docked.' And there was no getting away from it. To add to the horror, poor Rex's tail must be *bitten* off. Why bitten? we asked aghast. We were assured that biting was the only way. A man would take the little tail and just nip it through with his teeth, at a certain joint. My father lifted his lips and bared his incisors, to suit the description. We shuddered. But we were in the hands of fate.

Rex was carried away, and a man called Rowbotham bit off the superfluity of his tail in the Nag's Head, for a quart of best and bitter. We lamented our poor diminished puppy, but agreed to find him more manly and *comme il faut.* We should always have been ashamed of his little whip of a tail, if it had not been shortened. My father said it had made a man of him.

Perhaps it had. For now his true nature came out. And his true nature, like so much else, was dual. First he was a fierce, canine little beast, a beast of rapine and blood. He longed to hunt, savagely. He lusted to set his teeth in his prey. It was no joke with him. The old canine Adam stood first in him, the dog with fangs and glaring eyes. He flew at us when we annoyed him. He flew at all intruders, particularly the postman. He was almost a peril to the neighbourhood. But not quite. Because close second in his nature stood that fatal need to love, the *besoin d'aimer* which at last makes an end of liberty. He had a terrible, terrible necessity to love, and this trammelled the native, savage hunting beast which he was. He was torn between two great impulses: the native impulse to hunt and kill, and the strange, secondary, supervening impulse to love and obey. If he had been left to my father and mother, he would have run wild and got himself shot. As it was, he loved us children with a fierce, joyous love. And we loved him.

When we came home from school we would see him standing at the end of the entry, cocking his head wistfully at the open country in front of him, and meditating whether to be off or not: a white, inquiring little figure, with green savage freedom in front of him. A cry from a far distance from one of us, and like a bullet he hurled himself down the road, in a mad game. Seeing him coming, my sister invariably turned and fled, shrieking with delighted terror. And he would leap straight up her back, and bite her and tear her clothes. But it was only an ecstasy of savage love, and she knew it. She didn't care if he tore her pinafores. But my mother did.

My mother was maddened by him. He was a little demon. At the least provocation, he flew. You had only to sweep the floor, and he bristled and sprang at the broom. Nor would he let go. With his scruff erect and his nostrils snorting rage, he would turn up the whites of his eyes at my mother, as she wrestled at the other end of the broom. 'Leave go, sir, leave go!' She wrestled and stamped her foot, and he answered with horrid growls. In the end it was she who had to let go. Then she flew at him, and he flew at her. All the time we had him, he was within a hair's-breadth of savagely biting her. And she knew it. Yet he always kept sufficient self-control.

We children loved his temper. We would drag the bones from his mouth, and put him into such paroxysms of rage that he would twist his head right over and lay it on the ground upside-down, because he didn't know what to do with himself, the savage was so strong in him and he must fly at us. 'He'll fly at your throat one of these days,' said my father. Neither he nor my mother dared have touched Rex's bone. It was enough to see him bristle and roll the whites of his eyes when they came near. How near he must have been to driving his teeth right into us, cannot be told. He was a horrid sight snarling and crouching at us. But we only laughed and rebuked him. And he would whimper in the sheer torment of his need to attack us.

He never did hurt us. He never hurt anybody, though the neighbourhood was terrified of him. But he took to hunting. To my mother's disgust, he would bring large dead bleeding rats and lay them on the hearth-rug, and she had to take them up on a shovel. For he would not remove them. Occasionally he brought a mangled rabbit, and sometimes, alas, fragmentary poultry. We were in terror of prosecution. Once he came home bloody and feathery and rather sheepish-looking. We cleaned him and questioned him and abused him. Next day we heard of six dead ducks. Thank heaven no one had seen him.

But he was disobedient. If he saw a hen he was off, and calling would not bring him back. He was worst of all with my father, who would take him walks on Sunday morning. My mother would not walk a yard with him. Once, walking with my father, he rushed off at some sheep in a field. My father yelled in vain. The dog was at the sheep, and meant business. My father crawled through the hedge, and was upon him in time. And now the man was in a paroxysm of rage. He dragged the little beast into the road and thrashed him with a walking stick.

'Do you know you're thrashing that dog unmercifully?' said a passerby.

'Ay, an' mean to,' shouted my father.

The curious thing was that Rex did not respect my father

any the more, for the beatings he had from him. He took much more heed of us children, always.

But he let us down also. One fatal Saturday he disappeared. We hunted and called, but no Rex. We were bathed, and it was bed-time, but we would not go to bed. Instead we sat in a row in our nightdresses on the sofa. And wept without stopping. This drove our mother mad.

'Am I going to put up with it? Am I? And all for that hateful little beast of a dog! He shall go! If he's not gone now, he shall go.'

Our father came in late, looking rather queer, with his hat over his eye. But in his staccato tippled fashion he tried to be consoling.

'Never mind, my duckie, I s'll look for him in the morning.'

Sunday came – oh, such a Sunday. We cried, and didn't eat. We scoured the land, and for the first time realised how empty and wide the earth is, when you're looking for something. My father walked for many miles – all in vain. Sunday dinner, with rhubarb pudding, I remember, and an atmosphere of abject misery that was unbearable.

'Never,' said my mother, 'never shall an animal set foot in this house again, while I live. I knew what it would be! I knew.'

The day wore on, and it was the black gloom of bedtime, when we heard a scratch and an impudent little whine at the door. In trotted Rex, mud-black, disreputable, and impudent. His air of offhand 'How d'ye do!' was indescribable. He trotted around with *suffisance*, wagging his tail as if to say, 'Yes, I've come back. But I didn't need to. I can carry on remarkably well by myself.' Then he walked to his water, and drank noisily and ostentatiously. It was rather a slap in the eye for us.

He disappeared once or twice in this fashion. We never knew where he went. And we began to feel that his heart was not so golden as we had imagined it.

But one fatal day reappeared my uncle and the dog-cart. He whistled to Rex, and Rex trotted up. But when he wanted to examine the lusty, sturdy dog, Rex became suddenly still, then sprang free. Quite jauntily he trotted round – but out of reach of my uncle. He leaped up, licking our faces, and trying to make us play.

'Why, what ha' you done wi' the dog – you've made a fool of him. He's softer than grease. You've ruined him. You've made a damned fool of him,' shouted my uncle.

Rex was captured and hauled off to the dog-cart and tied to the seat. He was in a frenzy. He yelped and shrieked and struggled, and was hit on the head, hard, with the butt-end of my uncle's whip, which only made him struggle more frantically. So we saw him driven away, our beloved Rex, frantically, madly fighting to get to us from the high dog-cart, and being knocked down, while we stood in the street in mute despair.

After which, black tears, and a little wound which is still alive in our hearts.

I saw Rex only once again, when I had to call just once at The Good Omen. He must have heard my voice, for he was upon me in the passage before I knew where I was. And in the instant I knew how he loved us. He really loved us. And in the same instant there was my uncle with a whip, beating and kicking him back, and Rex cowering, bristling, snarling.

My uncle swore many oaths, how we had ruined the dog for ever, made him vicious, spoiled him for showing purposes, and been altogether a pack of mard-soft fools not fit to be trusted with any dog but a gutter-mongrel.

Poor Rex! We heard his temper was incurably vicious, and he had to be shot.

And it was our fault. We had loved him too much, and he had loved us too much. We never had another pet.

It is a strange thing, love. Nothing but love has made the dog lose his wild freedom, to become the servant of man. And this very servility or completeness of love makes him a term of deepest contempt – 'You dog!'

We should not have loved Rex so much, and he should not have loved us. There should have been a measure. We tended, all of us, to overstep the limits of our own natures. He should have stayed outside human limits, we should have stayed outside canine limits. Nothing is more fatal than the disaster of too much love. My uncle was right, we had ruined the dog.

My uncle was a fool, for all that.

A Prelude

'Sweet is pleasure after pain ...'

In the kitchen of a small farm a little women sat cutting bread and butter. The glow of the clear, ruddy fire was on her shining cheek and white apron; but grey hair will not take the warm caress of firelight.

She skilfully spread the softened butter, and cut off great slices from the floury loaf in her lap. Already two plates were piled, but she continued to cut.

Outside the naked ropes of the creeper tapped and lashed at the window.

The grey-haired mother looked up, and setting the butter on the hearth, rose and went to look out. The sky was heavy and grey as she saw it in the narrow band over the near black wood. So she turned and went to look through the tiny window which opened from the deep recess on the opposite side of the room. The northern sky was blacker than ever.

She turned away with a little sigh, and took a duster from the red, shining warming-pan to take the bread from the oven. Afterwards she laid the table for five.

There was a rumbling and a whirring in the corner, and the clock struck five. Like clocks in many farmers' kitchens, it was more than half an hour fast. The little woman hurried about, bringing milk and other things from the dairy; lifting the potatoes from the fire, peeping through the window anxiously. Very often her neck ached with watching the gate for a sign of approach.

There was a click of the yard gate. She ran to the window, but turned away again, and, catching up the blue enamelled teapot, dropped into it a handful of tea from the caddy, and poured on the water. A clinking scrape of iron shod boots sounded outside, then the door opened with a burst as a burly, bearded man entered. He drooped at the shoulders, and leaned forward as a man who has worked heavily all his life.

'Hello, mother,' he said loudly and cheerfully. 'Am I first? Aren't any of the lads down yet? Fred will be here in a minute.'

'I wish they would come,' said his wife, 'or else it'll rain before they're here.'

'Ay,' he assented, 'it's begining, and it's cold rain an' all. Bit of sleet, I think,' and he sat down heavily in his armchair, looking at his wife as she knelt and turned the bread, and took a large jar of stewed apples from the oven.

'Well mother,' he said with a pleasant comfortable little smile, 'here's another Christmas for you and me. They keep passing us by.'

'Ay,' she answered, the effects of her afternoon's brooding now appearing. 'They come and go, but they never find us any better off.'

'It seems so,' he said, a shade of regret appearing momentarily over his cheerfulness. 'This year we've certainly had some very bad luck. But we keep straight – and we never regret that Christmas, see, it's twenty-seven years since – twenty-seven years.'

'No, perhaps not, but there's Fred as hasn't had above three pounds for the whole year's work, and the other two at the pit.'

'Well, what can I do? If I hadn't lost the biggest part of the hay, and them two beast –'

'If –! Besides what prospects has he? Here he is working year in year out for you and getting nothing at the end of it. When you were his age, when you were 25, you were married and had two children. How can he ask anybody to marry him?'

'I don't know that he wants to. He's fairly contented. Don't be worrying about him and upsetting him. He'd only go and leave us if he got married. Besides, we may have a good year next year, and we can make this up.'

'Ay, so you say.'

'Don't fret yourself to-night, lass. It's true things haven't gone as we hoped they would. I never thought to see you doing all the work you have to do, but we've been very comfortable, all things considered, haven't we?'

'I never thought to see my first lad a farm labourer at 25, and the other two in the pit. Two of my sons in the pit!'

'I'm sure I've done what I could, and' – but they heard a scraping outside, and he said no more.

The eldest son tramped in, his great boots and his leggings all covered with mud. He took off his wet overcoat, and stood on the hearthrug, his hands spread out behind him in the warmth of the fire.

Looking smilingly at his mother, as she moved about the kitchen, he said:

'You do look warm and cosy, mother. When I was coming up with the last load I thought of you trotting about in that big, white apron, getting tea ready, watching the weather. There are the lads. Aren't you quite contented now – prefectly happy?'

She laughed an odd little laugh, and poured out the tea. The boys came in from the pit, wet and dirty, with clean streaks down their faces where the rain had trickled. They changed their clothes and sat at the table. The elder was a big, heavy, loosely made fellow, with a long nose and chin, and comical wrinkling round his eyes. The younger, Arthur, was a handsome lad, dark-haired, with ruddy colour glowing through his dirt, and dark eyes. When he talked and laughed the red of his lips and whitness of his teeth and eyeballs stood out in startling contrast to the surrounding black.

'Mother, I'm glad to see thee,' he said, looking at her with frank, boyish affection.

'There mother, what more can you want?' asked her husband.

She took a bite of bread and butter, and looked up with a quaint, comical glance, as if she were given only her just dues, but for all that it pleased and amused her, only she was half shy, and a grain doubtful.

'Lad,' said Henry, 'it's Christmas Eve. The fire ought to burn its brightest.'

'Yes, I will have just another potato, seeing as Christmas is the time for feeding. What are we going to do? Are we going to have a party, mother?'

'Yes, if you want one.'

'Party,' laughed the father, 'who'd come?'

'We might ask somebody. We could have Nellie Wycherley, who used to come, an' David Garton.'

'We shall not do for Nellie nowadays,' said the father. 'I saw her on Sunday morning on the top road. She was drivin' home with another young woman, an' she stopped an' asked me if we'd got any holly with berries on, an' I said we hadn't.'

Fred looked up from the book he was reading over tea. He had dark brown eyes, something like his mother's, and they always drew attention when he turned them on anyone.

'There is a tree covered in the wood,' he said.

'Well,' answered the irrepressible Henry, 'that's not ours, is it? An' if she's got that proud she won't come near to see us, am I goin' choppin' trees down for her? If she'd come here an' say she wanted a bit, I'd fetch her half the wood in. But when she sits in the trap and looks down on you an' asks, "Do you happen to hev a bush of berried holly in your hedges? Preston can't find a sprig to decorate the house, and I hev some people coming down from town," then I tell her we're crying because we've none to decorate ouselves, and we want it the more 'cause nobody's coming, neither from th' town nor th' country, an' we're likely to forget it's Christmas if we've neither folks nor things to remind us.'

'What did she say?' asked the mother.

'She said she was sorry, an' I told her not to bother, it's better lookin' at folks than at bits o' holly. The other lass was laughing, an' she wanted to know what folks. I told her any as hadn't got more pricks than a holly bush to keep you off.'

'Ha! ha!' laughed the father; 'did she take it?'

'The other girl nudged her, and they both began a laughing. Then Nellie told me to send down the guysers to-night. I said I would, but they're not going now.'

'Why not?' asked Fred.

'Billy Simpson's got a gathered face, an' Wardy's gone to Nottingham.'

'The company down at Ramsley Mill will have nobody to laugh at to-night,' said Arthur.

'Tell ye what!' exclaimed Henry, 'we'll go.'

'How can we, three of us?' asked Arthur.

'Well,' persisted Henry, 'we could dress up so as they'd niver know us, an' hae a bit o' fun. Hey!' he suddenly shouted to Fred, who was reading, and taking no notice. 'Hey, we're going to the Mill guysering.'

'Who is?' asked the elder brother, somewhat surprised.

'You, an' me, an' our Arthur. I'll be Beelzebub.'

Here he distorted his face to look diabolic, so that everybody roared.

'Go,' said his father, 'you'll make our fortunes.'

'What!' he exclaimed, 'by making a fool of myself? They say fools for luck. What fools wise folk must be. Well, I'll be the devil – are you shocked, mother? What will you be, Arthur?'

'I don't care,' was the answer. 'We can put some of that red paint on our faces, and some soot, they'd never know us. Shall we go, Fred?'

'I don't know.'

'Why, I should like to see her with her company, to see if she has very fine airs. We could leave some holly for her in the scullery.'

'All right, then.'

After tea all helped with the milking and feeding. Then Fred took a hedge knife and a hurricane lamp and went into the wood to cut some of the richly berried holly. When he got back he found his brothers roaring with laughter before the mirror. They were smeared with red and black, and had fastened on grotesque horsehair moustaches, so that they were entirely unrecognisable.

'Oh, you are hideous,' cried their mother. 'Oh, it is shameful to disfigure the work of the Almighty like that!'

Fred washed and proceeded to dress. They could not persuade him to use paint or soot. He rolled his sleeves up to the shoulder, and wrapped himself in a great striped horse rug. Then he tied a white cloth round his head, as the Bedouins do, and pulled out his moustache to fierce points. He looked at himself with approval, took an old sword from the wall, and held it in one naked, muscular arm.

'Decidedly,' he thought, 'it is very picturesque, and I look very fine.'

'Oh, that is grand,' exclaimed his mother, as he entered the kitchen. His dark eyes glowed with pleasure to hear her say it. He seemed somewhat excited, this bucolic young man. His tanned skin shone rich and warm under the white cloth, its coarseness hidden by the yellow lamplight. His eyes glittered like a true Arab's, and it was to be noticed that the muscles of his sunbrowned arm were tense with the grip of the broad hand.

It was remarkable how the dark folds of the rug and the flowing burnouse glorified this young farmer, who, in his best clothes looked awkward and ungainly, and whose face a linen collar showed coarse, owing to exposure to the weather, and long application to heavy labour.

They set out to cross the two of their own fields, and two of their neighbour's which separated their home from the mill. A few uncertain flakes of snow were eddying down, melting as they settled. The ground was wet, and the night very dark. But they knew the way well, and were soon at the gate leading to the mill yard. The dog began to bark furiously, but they called to him, 'Trip, Trip,' and knowing their voices, he was quieted.

Henry gave a thundering knock, and bawled in stentorian tones,

'Dun yer want guysers?'

A man came to the door, very tall, very ungainly, very swarthy.

'We non want yer,' he said, talking down his nose.

'Here comes Beelzebub,' banged away Henry, thumping a pan which he carried. 'Here comes Beelzebub, an' he's come to th' right place.'

A big, bonny farm girl came to the door.

'Who is it?' she asked.

'Beelzebub, you know him well,' was the answer.

'I'II ask Miss Ellen if she wants you.'

Henry winked a red and black wink at the maid, saying, 'Never keep Satan on the doorstep,' and he stepped into the scullery.

The girl ran away, and soon was heard a laughing, and bright talking of women's voices drawing nearer to the kitchen.

'Tell them to come in,' said a voice.

The three trooped in, and glanced round the big kitchen. They could only see Betty, seated as near to them as possible on the squab, her father, black and surly, in his armchair, and two women's figures in the deep shadows of one of the great ingle-nook seats.

'Ah,' said Beelzebub, 'this is a bit more like it, a bit hotter. The Devil feels at home here.'

They began the ludicrous old Christmas play that everyone knows so well. Beelzebub acted with much force, much noise, and some humour. St. George, that is Fred, played his part with zeal and earnestness most amusing, but at one of the most crucial moments he entirely forgot his speech, which, however, was speedily rectified by Beelzebub. Arthur was nervous and awkward, so that Beelzebub supplied him with most of his speeches.

After much horseplay, stabbing, falling on the floor, bangings of dripping-pans and ludicrous striving to fill in the blanks, they came to an end.

They waited in silence.

'Well, what next,' asked a voice from the shadows.

'It's your turn,' said Beelzebub.

'What do you want?'

'As little as you have the heart to give.'

'But,' said another voice, one they knew well, 'We have no heart to give at all.'

'You did not know your parts well,' said Blanche, the stranger. 'The big fellow in the blanket deserves nothing.'

'What about me?' asked Arthur.

'You,' answered the same voice, 'oh, you're a nice boy, and a lady's; thanks are enough reward for you.'

He blushed, and muttered something unintelligible.

'There'll be the Devil to pay,' suggested Beelzebub.

'Give the Devil his dues, Nell,' said Blanche, choking again with laughter. Nellie threw a large silver coin on to the flagstone floor, but she was nervous, and it rolled to the feet of Preston in his armchair.

''Alf-a-crern!' he exclaimed, 'gie 'em thripence, an' they're non worth that much.'

This was too much for the chivalrous St George. He could bear no longer to stand in this ridiculous garb before his scornful lady-love and her laughing friend.

He snatched off his burnouse and his robe, flung them over one arm, and with the other caught back Beelzebub, who would have gone to pick up the money. There he stood, St George metamorphosed into a simple young farmer, with ruffled curly black hair, a heavy frown and bare arms.

'Won't you let him have it?' asked Blanche. 'Well, what do you want?' she continued.

'Nothing, thanks. I'm sorry we troubled you.'

'Come on,' he said, drawing the reluctant Beelzebub, and the three made their exit. Blanche laughed and laughed again to see the discomfited knight tramp out, rolling down his shirt sleeves.

Nellie did not laugh. Seeing him turn, she saw him again as a child, before her father had made money by his cattle-dealing, when she was a poor, wild little creature. But her father had grown rich, and the mill was a big farm, and when the old cattle dealer had died, she became sole mistress. Then

Preston, their chief man, came with Betty and Sarah, to live in, and take charge of the farm.

Nellie had seen little of her old friends since then. She had stayed a long time in town, and when she called on them after her return found them cool and estranged. So she had not been again, and now it was almost a year since she had spoken many words to Fred.

Her brief meditations were disturbed by a scream from Betty in the scullery, followed by the wild rush of that damsel into the kitchen.

'What's up?' asked her father.

'There's somebody there got hold of my legs.'

Nellie felt suddenly her own loneliness. Preston struck a match and investigated. He returned with a bunch of glittering holly, thick with scarlet berries.

'Here's yer somebody,' said he, flinging the bunch down on the table.

'Oh, that is pretty!' exclaimed Blanche. Nellie rose, looked, then hurried down the passage to the sitting-room, followed by her friend. There, to the consternation of Blanche, she sat down and began to cry.

'Whatever is the matter?' asked Blanche.

It was some time before she had a reply, then, 'It's so miserable,' faltered Nellie, 'and so lonely. I do think Will and Harry and Louie and all the others were mean not to come, then this wouldn't have happened. It was such a shame – such a shame.'

'What was a shame?' asked Blanche.

'Why, when he had got me that holly, and come down to see –' she ended, blushing.

'Who do you mean – the Bedouin?'

'And I had not seen him for months, and he will think I am just a mean, proud thing.'

'You don't mean to say you care for him!'

Nellie's tears began to flow again. 'I do, and I wish this miserable farm and bit of money had never come between us. He'll never come again, never, I know.'

'Then,' said Blanche, 'you must go to him.'

'Yes, and I will.'

'Come along, then.'

In the meantime the disappointed brothers had reached home. Fred had thrown down his Bedouin wardrobe, and put on his coat muttering something about having a walk up to the village. Then he had gone out, his mother's eyes watching his exit with helpless grief, his father looking over his spectacles in a half-surprised paternal sympathy. However, they heard him tramp down the yard and enter the barn, and they knew he would soon recover. Then the lads went out, and nothing was heard in the kitchen save the beat of the clock and the rustle of the newspaper, or the rattle of the board, as the mother rolled out paste for the mince-pies.

In the pitch-dark barn, the rueful Bedouin told himself that he expected no other than this, and that it was high time he ceased fooling himself with fancies, that he was well-cured, that even had she invited him to stay, how could he; how could he have asked her; she must think he wanted badly to become master of Ramsley Mill. What a fool he had been to go – what a fool!

'But,' he argued, 'let her think what she likes. I don't care. She may remember if she can that I used to sole her boots with my father's leather, and she went home in mine. She can remember that my mother taught her how to write and sew decently. I should think she must sometimes.'

Then he admitted to himself that he was sure she did not forget. He could feel quite well that she was wishing that this long estrangement might cease.

'But,' came the question, 'why doesn't she end it? Pah, it's only my conceit; she thinks more of those glib, grinning fellows from the clerks' stools. Let her, what do I care!'

Suddenly he heard voices from the field at the back, and sat up listening.

'Oh, it's a regular slough,' said someone. 'We can never get through the gate. See, let us climb the stackyard fence.

They've put some new rails in. Can you manage, Blanche? Here, just between the lilac bush and the stack. What a blessing they keep Chris at the front! Mind, bend under this plum tree. Dare we go, Blanche?'

'Go on, go on,' whispered Blanche, and they crept up to the tiny window, through which the lamplight streamed uninterrupted. Fred stole out of the barn, and hid behind the great water-butt. He saw them stoop and creep to the window and peep through.

In the kitchen sat the father, smoking and appearing to read, but really staring into the fire. The mother was putting the top crusts on the little pies, but she was interrupted by the need to wipe her eyes.

'Oh, Blanche,' whispered Nellie, 'he's gone out.'

'It looks like it,' assented the other.

'Perhaps he's not, though,' resumed the former bravely. 'He's very likely only in the parlour.'

'That's all right, then,' said Blanche. 'I thought we should have seen him looking so miserable. But, of course, he wouldn't let his mother see it.'

'Certainly not,' said Nellie.

Fred chuckled.

'But,' she continued doubtfully, 'if he has gone out, whatever shall we do? What can we tell his mother?'

'Tell her we came up for fun.'

'But if he's out?'

'Stay till he comes home.'

'If it's late?'

'It's Christmas Eve.'

'Perhaps he doesn't care after all.'

'You think he does, so do I; and you're quite sure you want him.'

'You know I do, Blanche, and I always have done.'

'Let us begin, then.'

'What? "Good King Wenceslaus?"'

The mother and father started as the two voices suddenly

began to carol outside. She would have run to the door, but her husband waved her excitedly back. 'Let them finish,' he said, his eyes shining. 'Let them finish.'

The girls had retired from the window lest they should be seen, and stood near the water-butt. When the old carol was finished, Nellie began the beautiful song of Giordani's: –

> Turn once again, heal thou my pain,
> Parted from thee, my heart is sore.

As she sang she stood holding a bough of the old plum tree, so close to Fred that by leaning forward he could have touched her coat. Carried away by the sweet pathos of her song, he could hardly refrain from rising and flinging his arms round her.

She finished, the door opened, showing a little woman holding out her hands.

Both girls made a motion towards her, but – 'Nell, Nell,' he whispered, and caught her in his arms. She gave a little cry of alarm and delight. Blanche stepped into the kitchen, and shut the door, laughing.

She sat in the low rocking-chair swinging to and fro in a delighted excitement, chattering brightly about a hundred things. And with a keen woman's eye she noticed the mother put her hands on her husband's as she sat on the sofa by his chair, and saw him hold the shining stiffened hand in one of his, and stroke it with old, undiminished affection.

Soon the two came in, Nellie all blushing. Without a word she ran and kissed the little mother, lingering a moment over her before she turned to the quiet embrace of the father. Then she took off her hat, and brushed back the brown tendrils all curled so prettily by the damp.

Already she was at home.

Lessford's Rabbits

On Tuesday mornings I have to be at school at half past eight to administer the free breakfasts. Dinners are given in the canteen in one of the mean streets, where the children feed in a Church Mission room appropriately adorned by Sunday School cartoons showing the blessing of the little ones, and the feeding of the five thousand. We serve breakfasts, however, in school, in the wood-work room high up under the roof.

Tuesday morning sees me rushing up the six short flights of stone stairs, at twenty-five minutes to nine. It is my disposition to be late. I generally find a little crowd of children waiting in the 'art' room – so called because it is surrounded with a strip of blackboard too high for the tallest boy to reach – which is a sort of ante-room to the workshop where breakfast is being prepared. I hasten through the little throng to see if things are ready. There are two big girls putting out the basins, and another one looking in the pan to see if the milk is boiling. The room is warm, and seems more comfortable because the windows are high up under the beams of the slanting roof and the walls are all panelled with ruddy gold, varnished wood. The work bench is in the form of three sides of a square – or of an oblong – as the dining tables of the ancients used to be, I believe. At one of the extremities are the three vises, and at the other the great tin pan, like a fish kettle, standing on a gas ring. When the boys' basins are placed along the outer edge of the bench, the girls' on the inner, and the infants' on the lockers against the wall, we are ready. I look at the two rows of assorted basins, and think of the three bears. Then I admit the thirty, who bundle to their places and stand in position, girls on the inside facing boys on the outside, and quaint little infants with their toes kicking the lockers along the walls.

Last week the Infant mistress did not come up, so I was

alone. She is an impressive woman, who always commands the field. I stand in considerable awe of her. I feel like a reckless pleasure boat with one extravagant sail misbehaving myself in the track of a heavy earnest coaster when she bears down on me. I was considerably excited to find myself in sole charge. As I ushered in the children, the caretaker, a little fierce-eyed man with hollow cheeks and walrus moustache, entered with the large basket full of chunks of bread. He glared around without bidding me good morning.

'Miss Culloch not come?' he asked.

'As you see,' I replied.

He grunted, and put down the basket. Then he drew himself up like a fiery prophet, and stretching forth his hairy arm towards the opposite door, shouted loudly to the children:

'None of you's got to touch that other door there! You hear – you're to leave it alone!'

The children stared at him without answering.

'A brake as I'm making for these doors,' he said confidentially to me, thrusting forward his extraordinarily hairy lean arms, and putting two fingers of one hand into the palm of the other, as if to explain his invention. I bowed.

'Nasty things them swing doors' – he looked up at me with his fierce eyes, and suddenly swished aside his right arm:

'They come to like *that*!' he exclaimed, 'and a child's finger is cut off – clean!' – he looked at me for ratification. I bowed.

'It'll be a good thing, I think,' he concluded, considerably damped. I bowed again. Then he left me. The chief, almost the only duty of a caretaker, is to review the works of the head and of the staff, as a reviewer does books: at length and according to his superior light.

I told one of the girls to give three chunks of bread to each child, and, having fished a mysterious earwig out of the scalding milk, I filled the large enamelled jug – such as figures and has figured in the drawing lessons of every school in England, I suppose – and doled out the portions – about three-quarters of a pint per senior, and half a pint per infant. Everything was ready. I had to say grace. I dared not launch into the Infant mistress' formula, thanking the Lord for his goodness – 'and may we eat and drink to thine everlasting glory – Amen.' I looked at the boys, dressed in mouldering garments of remote men, at the girls with their rat-tailed hair, and at the infants, quaint little mites on whom I wished, but could not bring myself, to expend my handkerchief, and I wondered what I should say. The only other grace I knew was 'For these and for all good things may the Lord make us truly thankful.' But I wondered whom we should thank for the bad things. I was becoming desperate. I plunged:

'Ready now – hands together, close eyes. "Let us eat, drink and be merry, for tomorrow we die."' I felt myself flushing with confusion – what did I mean? But there was a universal clink of iron spoons on the basins, and a snuffling, slobbering sound of children feeding. They had not noticed, so it was all right. The infants were kneeling and squalling by the lockers, the boys were stretching wide their eyes and their mouths at the same time, to admit the spoon. They spilled the milk on their jackets and wiped it off with their sleeves, continuing to eat all the time.

'Don't slobber, lads, be decent,' I said, rebuking them from my superior sphere. They ate more carefully, glancing up at me when the spoon was at their mouths.

I began to count the number – nine boys, seven girls, and eleven infants. Not many. We could never get many boys to give in their names for free meals. I used to ask the Kelletts, who were pinched and pared thin with poverty:

'Are you sure you don't want either dinners or breakfasts, Kellett?'

He would look at me curiously, and say, with a peculiar small movement of his thin lips.

'No Sir.'

'But have you plenty – quite plenty?'

'Yes Sir' – he was very quiet, flushing at my questions.

None – or very few – of the boys could endure to accept the meals. Not many parents would submit to the indignity of the officer's inquirer and the boys, the most foolishly sensitive animals in the world, would, many of them, prefer to go short rather than to partake of charity meals of which all their school-mates were aware.

'Halket – where is Halket?' I asked.

'Please Sir, his mother's got work,' replied Lessford, one of my own boys, a ruddy, bonny lad – many of those at breakfast were pictures of health. Lessford was brown-skinned and had fine dark eyes. He was a reticent, irresponsible creature, with a radical incapacity to spell and to read and to draw, but who sometimes scored at arithmetic. I should think he came of a long line of unrelievedly poor people. He was skilled in street lore, and cute at arithmetic, but blunt and blind to everything that needed a little delicacy of perception. He had an irritating habit of looking at me furtively, with his handsome dark eyes, glancing covertly again and again. Yet he was not a sneak; he gave himself the appearance of one. He was a well-built lad, and he looked well in the blue jersey he wore – there were great holes at the elbows, showing the whitish shirt and a brown bit of Lessford. At breakfasts he was a great eater. He would have five solid pieces of bread, and then ask for more.

We gave them bread and milk one morning, cocoa and currant bread the next. I happened to go one cocoa morning to take charge. Lessford, I noticed, did not eat by any means so much as on bread mornings. I was surprised. I asked him if he did not care for currant loaf, but he said he did. Feeling curious, I asked the other teachers what they thought of him. Mr Hayward, who took a currant bread morning, said he was sure the boy had a breakfast before he came to school; – Mr Jephson, who took a milk morning, said the lad was voracious, that it amused him to try to feed him up. I watched – turning suddenly to ask if anyone wanted a little more milk, and glancing over the top of the milk pan as I was emptying it.

I caught him: I saw him push a piece of bread under his jersey, glancing furtively with a little quiver of apprehension up at me. I did not appear to notice, but when he was going downstairs I followed him and asked him to go into the class-room with me. I closed the door and sat down at my table: he stood hanging his head and marking with his foot on the floor. He came to me, very slowly, when I bade him. I put my hand on his jersey, and felt something underneath. He did not resist me, and I drew it out. It was his cap. He smiled, he could not help it, at my discomfiture. Then he pulled his lips straight and looked sulky. I tried again – and this time I found three pieces of bread in a kind of rough pocket inside the waist of his trousers. He looked at them blackly as I arranged them on the table before him, flushing under his brown skin.

'What does this mean?' I asked. He hung his head, and would not answer.

'You may as well tell me – what do you want this for?'

'Eat,' he muttered, keeping his face bent. I put my hand under his chin and lifted up his face. He shut his eyes, and tried to move his face aside, as if from a very strong light which hurt him.

'That is not true,' I said. 'I know perfectly well it is not true. You have a breakfast before you come. You do not come to eat. You come to take the food away.'

'I never!' he exclaimed sulkily.

'No,' I said. 'You did not take any yesterday. But the day before you did.'

'I never, I never!!' he declared, more emphatically, in the tone of one who scores again. I considered.

'Oh no – the day before was Sunday. Let me see. You took some on Thursday – yes, that was the last time – You took four or five pieces of bread –' I hung fire; he did not contradict; 'five, I believe,' I added. He scraped his toe on the ground. I had guessed aright. He could not deny the definite knowledge of a number.

But I could not get another word from him. He stood and

heard all I had to say, but he would not look up, or answer anything. I felt angry.

'Well,' I said, 'if you come to breakfasts any more, you will be reported.'

Next day, when asked why he was absent from breakfast, he said his father had got a job.

He was a great nuisance for coming with dirty boots. Evidently he went roaming over fields and everywhere. I concluded he must have a strain of gipsy in him, a mongrel form common in the south of London. Halket was his great friend. They never played together at school, and they had no apparent common interests. Halket was a debonair, clever lad who gave great promise of turning out a neer-do-well. He was very lively, soon moved from tears to laughter; Lessford was an inveterate sulker. Yet they always hung together.

One day my bread-stealer arrived at half past two, when the register was closed. He was sweating, dishevelled, and his breast was heaving. He gave no word of explanation, but stood near the great blackboard, his head dropped, one leg loosely apart, panting.

'Well!' I exclaimed, 'this is a nice thing! What have you to say?' I rose from my chair.

Evidently he had nothing to say.

'Come on,' I said finally. 'No foolery! Let me hear it.' He knew he would have to speak. He looked up at me, his dark eyes blazing:

'My rabbits has all gone!' he cried, as a man would announce his wife and children slain. I heard Halket exclaim. I looked at him. He was half-out of the desk, his mercurial face blank with dismay.

'Who's 'ad 'em?' he said, breathing the words almost in a whisper.

'Did you leave th' door open?' Lessford bent forward like a serpent about to strike as he asked his. Halket shook his head solemnly:

'No! I've not been near 'em today.'

There was a pause. It was time for me to reassume my position of authority. I told them both to sit down, and we continued the lesson. Halket crept near his comrade and began to whisper to him, but he received no response. Lessford sulked fixedly, not moving his head for more than an hour.

At playtime I began to question Halket: 'Please Sir – we had some rabbits in a place on the allotments. We used to gather manure for a man, and he let us have half of his tool-house in the garden –.'

'How many had you – rabbits?'

'Please Sir – they varied. When we had young ones we used to have sixteen sometimes. We had two brown does and a black buck.'

I was somewhat taken back by this.

'How long have you had them?'

'A long time now Sir. We've had six lots of young ones.'

'And what did you do with them?'

'Fatten them, Sir' – he spoke with a little triumph, but he was reluctant to say much more.

'And what did you fatten them on?'

The boy glanced swiftly at me. He reddened, and for the first time became confused.

'Green stuff, what we had given us out of the gardens, and what we got out of the fields.'

'And bread,' I answered quietly.

He looked at me. He saw I was not angry, only ironical. For a few moments he hesitated, whether to lie or not. Then he admitted, very subdued:

'Yes Sir.'

'And what did you do with the rabbits?' – he did not answer – 'Come, tell me. I can find out whether or not.'

'Sold them,' – he hung his head guiltily.

'Who did the selling?'

'I, Sir – to a greengrocer.'

'For how much?'

'Eightpence each.'

'And did your mothers know?'

'No Sir.' He was very subdued and guilty.

'And what did you do with the money?'

'Go to the Empire – generally.'

I asked him a day or two later if they had found the rabbits. They had not. I asked Halket what he supposed had become of them.

'Please Sir – I suppose somebody must 'a stole them. The door was not broken. You could open our padlock with a hair-pin. I suppose somebody must have come after us last night when we'd fed them. I think I know who it is, too, Sir.' He shook his head wisely – 'There's a place where you can get into the allotments off the field –'

A Lesson on a Tortoise

It was the last lesson on Friday afternoon, and this, with Standard VI, was Nature Study from half-past three till half-past four. The last lesson of the week is a weariness to teachers and scholars. It is the end; there is no need to keep up the tension of discipline and effort any longer, and, yielding to weariness, a teacher is spent.

But Nature Study is a pleasant lesson. I had got a big old tortoise, who had not yet gone to sleep, though November was darkening the early afternoon, and I knew the boys would enjoy sketching him. I put him under the radiator to warm while I went for a large empty shell that I had sawn in two to show the ribs of some ancient tortoise absorbed in his bony coat. When I came back I found Joe, the old reptile, stretching slowly his skinny neck, and looking with indifferent eyes at the two intruding boys who were kneeling beside him. I was too good-tempered to send them out again into the playground, too slack with the great relief of Friday afternoon. So I bade them put out the Nature books ready. I crouched to look at Joey, and stroked his horny, blunt head with my finger. He was quite lively. He spread out his legs and gripped the floor with his flat hand-like paws, when he slackened again as if from a yawn, dropping his head meditatively.

I felt pleased with myself, knowing that the boys would be delighted with the lesson. 'He will not want to walk,' I said to myself, 'and if he takes a sleepy stride, they'll be just in ecstasy, and I can easily calm him down to his old position.' So I anticipated their entry. At the end of playtime I went to bring them in. They were a small class of about thirty – my own boys. A difficult, mixed class, they were, consisting of six London Home boys, five boys from a fairly well-to-do Home for the children of actors, and a set of commoners varying from poor lads who hobbled to school, crippled by broken enormous boots, to boys who brought soft, light shoes to wear in school on snowy days. The Gordons were a difficult set; you could pick them out: crop haired, coarsely dressed lads, distrustful, always ready to assume the defensive. They would lie till it made my heart sick, if they were charged with offence, but they were willing, and would respond beautifully to an appeal. The actors were of different fibre: some gentle, a pleasure even to look at; others polite and obedient, but indifferent, covertly insolent and vulgar; all of them more or less gentlemanly.

The boys crowded round the table noisily as soon as they discovered Joe. 'Is he alive? – Look, his head's coming out! He'll bite you? – He *won't*!' – with much scorn – 'Please Sir, do tortoises bite?' I hurried them off to their seats in a little group in front, and pulled the table up to the desks. Joe kept fairly still. The boys nudged each other excitedly, making half audible remarks concerning the poor reptile, looking quickly from me to Joe and then to their neighbours. I set them sketching, but in their pleasure at the novelty they could not be still:

'Please Sir – shall we draw the marks on the shell? Please Sir, has he only got four toes?' – 'Toes!' echoes somebody, covertly delighted at the absurdity of calling the grains of claws 'toes'. 'Please Sir, he's moving – Please Sir!'

I stroked his neck and calmed him down:

'Now don't make me wish I hadn't brought him. That's enough. Miles – you shall go to the back and draw twigs if I hear you again! Enough now – be still, get on with the drawing, it's hard!'

I wanted peace for myself. They began to sketch diligently. I stood and looked across at the sunset, which I could see facing me through my window, a great gold sunset, very large and magnificent, rising up in immense gold beauty beyond the town, that was become a low dark strip of nothingness under the wonderful up-building of the western sky. The light, the thick, heavy golden sunlight which is only seen in its full dripping splendour in town, spread on the desks and the floor like gold lacquer. I lifted my hands, to take the sunlight on them, smiling faintly to myself, trying to shut my fingers over its tangible richness.

'Please Sir!' – I was interrupted – 'Please Sir, can we have rubbers?'

The question was rather plaintive. I had said they should have rubbers no more. I could not keep my stock, I could not detect the thief among them, and I was weary of the continual degradation of bullying them to try to recover what was lost among them. But it was Friday afternoon, very peaceful and happy. Like a bad teacher, I went back on my word:

'Well –!' I said, indulgently.

My monitor, a pale, bright, erratic boy, went to the cupboard and took out a red box.

'Please Sir!' he cried, then he stopped and counted again in the box. 'Eleven! There's only eleven, Sir, and there were fifteen when I put them away on Wednesday –!'

The class stopped, every face upturned. Joe sunk, and lay flat on his shell, his legs limp. Another of the hateful moments had come. The sunset was smeared out, the charm of the afternoon was smashed like a fair glass that falls to the floor. My nerves seemed to tighten, and to vibrate with sudden tension.

'Again!' I cried, turning to the class in passion, to the upturned faces, and the sixty watchful eyes.

'Again! I am sick of it, sick of it I am! A thieving, wretched set! – a skulking, mean lot!' I was quivering with anger and distress.

'Who is it? You must know! You are all as bad as one another, you hide it – a miserable –!' I looked round the class in great agitation. The 'Gordons' with their distrustful faces, were noticeable:

'Marples!' I cried to one of them, 'where are those rubbers?'

'I don't know where they are – I've never 'ad no rubbers' – he almost shouted back, with the usual insolence of his set. I was more angry:

'You must know! They're gone – they don't melt into air, they don't fly – who took them then? Rawson, do you know anything of them?'

'No Sir!' he cried, with impudent indignation.

'No, you intend to know nothing! Wood, have you any knowledge of these four rubbers?'

'No!' he shouted, with absolute insolence.

'Come here!' I cried, 'come here! Fetch the cane, Burton. We'll make an end, insolence and thieving and all.'

The boy dragged himself to the front of the class, and stood slackly, almost crouching, glaring at me. The rest of the 'Gordons' sat upright in their desks, like animals of a pack ready to spring. There was tense silence for a moment. Burton handed me the cane, and I turned from the class to Wood. I liked him best among the Gordons.

'Now my lad!' I said. 'I'll cane you for impudence first.'

He turned swiftly to me; tears sprang to his eyes.

'Well,' he shouted at me, 'you always pick on the Gordons – you're always on to us –!' This was so manifestly untrue that my anger fell like a bird shot in a mid-flight.

'Why!' I exclaimed, 'what a disgraceful untruth! I am always excusing you, letting you off –!'

'But you pick on us – you start on us – you pick on Marples, an' Rawson, an' on me. You always begin with the Gordons.'

'Well,' I answered, justifying myself, 'isn't it natural? Haven't you boys stolen – haven't these boys stolen – several times – and been caught?'

'That doesn't say as we do now,' he replied.

'How am I to know? You don't help me. How do I know? Isn't it natural to suspect you –?'

'Well, it's not us. We know who it is. Everybody knows who it is – only they won't tell.'

'Who know?' I asked.

'Why Rawson, and Maddock, and Newling, and all of 'em.'

I asked these boys if they could tell me. Each one shook his head, and said 'No Sir.' I went round the class. It was the same. They lied to me every one.

'You see,' I said to Wood.

'Well – they won't own up,' he said. 'I shouldn't 'a done if you hadn't 'a been goin' to cane me.'

This frankness was painful, but I preferred it. I made them all sit down. I asked Wood to write his knowledge on a piece of paper, and I promised not to divulge. He would not. I asked the boys he had named, all of them. They refused. I asked them again – I appealed to them.

'Let them all do it then!' said Wood. I tore up scraps of paper, and gave each boy one.

'Write on it the name of the boy you suspect. He is a thief and a sneak. He gives endless pain and trouble to us all. It is your duty.'

They wrote furtively, and quickly doubled up the papers. I collected them in the lid of the rubber box, and sat at the table to examine them. There was dead silence, they all watched me. Joe had withdrawn into his shell, forgotten.

A few papers were blank; several had 'I suspect nobody' – these I threw in the paper basket; two had the name of an old thief, and these I tore up; eleven bore the name of my assistant monitor a splendid, handsome boy, one of the oldest of the actors. I remembered how deferential and polite he had been when I had asked him, how ready to make barren suggestions; I remembered his shifty, anxious look during the questioning; I remembered how eager he had been to do things for me before the monitor came in the room. I knew it was he – without remembering.

'Well!' I said, feeling very wretched when I was convinced that the papers were right. 'Go on with the drawing.'

They were very uneasy and restless, but quiet. From time to time they watched me. Very shortly, the bell rang. I told the two monitors to collect up the things, and I sent the class home. We did not go into prayers. I, and they, were in no mood for hymns and the evening prayer of gratitude.

When the monitors had finished, and I had turned out all the lights but one, I sent home Curwen, and kept my assistant-monitor a moment.

'Ségar, do you know anything of my rubbers?'

'No Sir' – he had a deep, manly voice, and he spoke with earnest protestation – flushing.

'No? Nor my pencils – nor my two books?'

'No Sir! I know nothing about the books.'

'No? The pencils then –?'

'No Sir! Nothing! I don't know anything about them.'

'Nothing, Ségar?'

'No Sir.'

He hung his head, and looked so humiliated, a fine, handsome lad, that I gave it up. Yet I knew he would be dishonest again, when the opportunity arrived.

'Very well! You will not help as monitor any more. You will not come into the classroom until the class comes in – any more. You understand?'

'Yes Sir' – he was very quiet.

'Go along then.'

He went out, and silently closed the door. I turned out the last light, tried the cupboards, and went home.

I felt very tired, and very sick. The night had come up, the clouds were moving darkly, and the sordid streets near the school felt like disease in the lamplight.

The Shades of Spring

I

It was a mile nearer through the wood. Mechanically, Syson turned up by the forge and lifted the field-gate. The blacksmith and his mate stood still, watching the trespasser. But Syson looked too much a gentleman to be accosted. They let him go in silence across the small field to the wood.

There was not the least difference between this morning and those of the bright springs, six or eight years back. White and sandy-gold fowls still scratched round the gate, littering the earth and the field with feathers and scratched-up rubbish. Between the two thick holly bushes in the wood-hedge was the hidden gap, whose fence one climbed to get into the wood; the bars were scored just the same by the keeper's boots. He was back in the eternal.

Syson was extraordinarily glad. Like an uneasy spirit he had returned to the country of his past, and he found it waiting for him, unaltered. The hazel still spread glad little hands downwards, the bluebells here were still wan and few, among the lush grass and in shade of the bushes.

The path through the wood, on the very brow of a slope, ran winding easily for a time. All around were twiggy oaks, just issuing their gold, and floor spaces diapered with woodruff, with patches of dog-mercury and tufts of hyacinth. Two fallen trees still lay across the track. Syson jolted down a steep, rough slope, and came again upon the open land, this time looking north as through a great window in the wood. He stayed to gaze over the level fields of the hill-top, at the village which strewed the bare upland as if it had tumbled off the passing waggons of industry, and been forsaken. There was a stiff, modern, grey little church, and blocks and rows of red dwellings lying at random; at the back, the twinkling headstocks of the pit, and the looming pit-hill. All was naked and out-of-doors, not a tree! It was quite unaltered.

Syson turned, satisfied, to follow the path that sheered downhill into the wood. He was curiously elated, feeling himself back in an enduring vision. He started. A keeper was standing a few yards in front, barring the way.

'Where might you be going this road, sir?' asked the man. The tone of his question had a challenging twang. Syson looked at the fellow with an impersonal, observant gaze. It was a young man of four or five and twenty, ruddy and well favoured. His dark blue eyes now stared aggressively at the intruder. His black moustache, very thick, was cropped short over a small, rather soft mouth. In every other respect the fellow was manly and good-looking. He stood just above middle height; the strong forward thrust of his chest, and the perfect ease of his erect, self-sufficient body, gave one the feeling that he was taut with animal life, like the thick jet of a fountain balanced in itself. He stood with the butt of his gun on the ground, looking uncertainly and questioningly at Syson. The dark, restless eyes of the trespasser, examining the man and penetrating into him without heeding his office, troubled the keeper and made him flush.

'Where is Naylor? Have you got his job?' Syson asked.

'You're not from the House, are you?' inquired the keeper. It could not be, since everyone was away.

'No, I'm not from the House,' the other replied. It seemed to amuse him.

'Then might I ask where you were making for?' said the keeper, nettled.

'Where I am making for?' Syson repeated. 'I am going to Willey-Water Farm.'

'This isn't the road.'

'I think so. Down this path, past the well, and out by the white gate.'

'But that's not the public road.'

'I suppose not. I used to come so often, in Naylor's time, I had forgotten. Where is he, by the way?'

'Crippled with rheumatism,' the keeper answered reluctantly.

'Is he?' Syson exclaimed in pain.

'And who might you be?' asked the keeper, with a new intonation.

'John Adderley Syson; I used to live in Cordy Lane.'

'Used to court Hilda Millership?'

Syson's eyes opened with a pained smile. He nodded. There was an awkward silence.

'And you – who are you?' asked Syson.

'Arthur Pilbeam – Naylor's my uncle,' said the other.

'You live here in Nuttall?'

'I'm lodgin' at my uncle's – at Naylor's.'

'I see!'

'Did you say you was goin' down to Willey-Water?' asked the keeper.

'Yes.'

There was a pause of some moments, before the keeper blurted: '*I'm* courtin' Hilda Millership.'

The young fellow looked at the intruder with a stubborn defiance, almost pathetic. Syson opened new eyes.

'Are you?' he said, astonished. The keeper flushed dark.

'She and me are keeping company,' he said.

'I didn't know!' said Syson. The other man waited uncomfortably.

'What, is the thing settled?' asked the intruder.

'How, settled?' retorted the other sulkily.

'Are you going to get married soon, and all that?'

The keeper stared in silence for some moments, impotent.

'I suppose so,' he said, full of resentment.

'Ah!' Syson watched closely.

'I'm married myself,' he added, after a time.

'You are?' said the other incredulously.

Syson laughed in his brilliant, unhappy way.

'This last fifteen months,' he said.

The keeper gazed at him with wide, wondering eyes, apparently thinking back, and trying to make things out.

'Why, didn't you know?' asked Syson.

'No, I didn't,' said the other sulkily.

There was silence for a moment.

'Ah well!' said Syson, 'I will go on. I suppose I may.' The keeper stood in silent opposition. The two men hesitated in the open, grassy space, set around with small sheaves of sturdy bluebells; a little open platform on the brow of the hill. Syson took a few indecisive steps forward, then stopped.

'I say, how beautiful!' he cried.

He had come in full view of the downslope. The wide path ran from his feet like a river, and it was full of bluebells, save for a green winding thread down the centre, where the keeper walked. Like a stream the path opened into azure shallows at the levels, and there were pools of bluebells, with still the green thread winding through, like a thin current of ice-water through blue lakes. And from under the twig-purple of the bushes swam the shadowed blue, as if the flowers lay in flood water over the woodland.

'Ah, isn't it lovely!' Syson exclaimed; this was his past, the country he had abandoned, and it hurt him to see it so beautiful. Woodpigeons cooed overhead, and the air was full of the brightness of birds singing.

'If you're married, what do you keep writing to her for, and sending her poetry books and things?' asked the keeper. Syson stared at him, taken aback and humiliated. Then he began to smile.

'Well,' he said, 'I did not know about you . . .'

Again the keeper flushed darkly.

'But if you are married –' he charged.

'I am,' answered the other cynically.

Then, looking down the blue, beautiful path, Syson felt his own humiliation. 'What right *have* I to hang on to her?' he thought, bitterly self-contemptuous.

'She knows I'm married and all that,' he said.

'But you keep sending her books,' challenged the keeper.

Syson, silenced, looked at the other man quizzically, half pitying. Then he turned.

'Good day,' he said, and was gone. Now, everything irritated him: the two sallows, one all gold and perfume and murmur, one silver-green and bristly, reminded him, that here he had taught her about pollination. What a fool he was! What god-forsaken folly it all was!

'Ah well,' he said to himself; 'the poor devil seems to have a grudge against me. I'll do my best for him.' He grinned to himself, in a very bad temper.

II

The farm was less than a hundred yards from the wood's edge. The wall of trees formed the fourth side to the open quadrangle. The house faced the wood. With tangled emotions, Syson noted the plum blossom falling on the profuse, coloured primroses, which he himself had brought here and set. How they had increased! There were thick tufts of scarlet, and pink, and pale purple primroses under the plum trees. He saw somebody glance at him through the kitchen window, heard men's voices.

The door opened suddenly: very womanly she had grown! He felt himself going pale.

'You? – Addy!' she exclaimed, and stood motionless.

'Who?' called the farmer's voice. Men's low voices answered. Those low voices, curious and almost jeering, roused the tormented spirit in the visitor. Smiling brilliantly at her, he waited.

'Myself – why not?' he said.

The flush burned very deep on her cheek and throat.

'We are just finishing dinner,' she said.

'Then I will stay outside.' He made a motion to show that

he would sit on the red earthenware pipkin that stood near the door among the daffodils, and contained the drinking water.

'Oh no, come in,' she said hurriedly. He followed her. In the doorway, he glanced swiftly over the family, and bowed. Everyone was confused. The farmer, his wife, and the four sons sat at the coarsely laid dinner-table, the men with arms bare to the elbows.

'I am sorry I come at lunch-time,' said Syson.

'Hello, Addy!' said the farmer, assuming the old form of address, but his tone cold. 'How are you?'

And he shook hands.

'Shall you have a bit?' he invited the young visitor, but taking for granted the offer would be refused. He assumed that Syson was become too refined to eat so roughly. The young man winced at the imputation.

'Have you had any dinner?' asked the daughter.

'No,' replied Syson. 'It is too early. I shall be back at half-past one.'

'You call it lunch, don't you?' asked the eldest son, almost ironical. He had once been an intimate friend of this young man.

'We'll give Addy something when we've finished,' said the mother, an invalid, deprecating.

'No – don't trouble. I don't want to give you any trouble,' said Syson.

'You could allus live on fresh air an' scenery,' laughed the youngest son, a lad of nineteen.

Syson went round the buildings, and into the orchard at the back of the house, where daffodils all along the hedgerow swung like yellow, ruffled birds on their perches. He loved the place extraordinarily, the hills ranging round, with bear-skin woods covering their giant shoulders, and small red farms like brooches clasping their garments; the blue streak of water in the valley, the bareness of the home pasture, the sound of myriad-threaded bird-singing, which went mostly unheard. To his last day, he would dream of this place, when he felt the sun on his face, or saw the small handfuls of snow between the winter twigs, or smelt the coming of spring.

Hilda was very womanly. In her presence he felt constrained. She was twenty-nine, as he was, but she seemed to him much older. He felt foolish, almost unreal, beside her. She was so static. As he was fingering some shed plum blossom on a low bough, she came to the back door to shake the tablecloth. Fowls raced from the stackyard, birds rustled from the trees. Her dark hair was gathered up in a coil like a crown on her head. She was very straight, distant in her bearing. As she folded the cloth, she looked away over the hills.

Presently Syson returned indoors. She had prepared eggs and curd cheese, stewed gooseberries and cream.

'Since you will dine to-night,' she said, 'I have only given you a light lunch.'

'It is awfully nice,' he said. 'You keep a real idyllic atmosphere – your belt of straw and ivy buds.'

Still they hurt each other.

He was uneasy before her. Her brief, sure speech, her distant bearing, were unfamiliar to him. He admired again her grey-black eyebrows, and her lashes. Their eyes met. He saw, in the beautiful grey and black of her glance, tears and a strange light, and at the back of all, calm acceptance of herself, and triumph over him.

He felt himself shrinking. With an effort he kept up the ironic manner.

She sent him into the parlour while she washed the dishes. The long low room was refurnished from the Abbey sale, with chairs upholstered in claret-coloured rep, many years old, and an oval table of polished walnut, and another piano, handsome, though still antique. In spite of the strangeness, he was pleased. Opening a high cupboard let into the thickness of the wall, he found it full of his books, his old lesson-books, and volumes of verse he had sent her, English and German. The daffodils in the white window-bottoms shone across the room, he could almost feel their rays. The old glamour caught him again. His youthful water-colours on the wall no longer made him grin; he remembered how fervently he had tried to paint for her, twelve years before.

She entered, wiping a dish, and he saw again the bright, kernel-white beauty of her arms.

'You are quite splendid here,' he said, and their eyes met.

'Do you like it?' she asked. It was the old, low, husky tone of intimacy. He felt a quick change beginning in his blood. It was the old, delicious sublimation, the thinning, almost the vaporising of himself, as if his spirit were to be liberated.

'Aye,' he nodded, smiling at her like a boy again. She bowed her head.

'This was the countess's chair,' she said in low tones. 'I found her scissors down here between the padding.'

'Did you? Where are they?'

Quickly, with a lilt in her movement, she fetched her work-basket, and together they examined the long-shanked old scissors.

'What a ballad of dead ladies!' he said, laughing, as he fitted his fingers into the round loops of the countess's scissors.

'I knew you could use them,' she said, with certainty. He looked at his fingers, and at the scissors. She meant his fingers were fine enough for the small-looped scissors.

'That is something to be said for me,' he laughed, putting the scissors aside. She turned to the window. He noticed the fine, fair down on her cheek and her upper lip, and her soft, white neck, like the throat of a nettle flower, and her forearms, bright as newly blanched kernels. He was looking at her with new eyes, and she was a different person to him. He did not know her. But he could regard her objectively now.

'Shall we go out awhile?' she asked.

'Yes!' he answered. But the predominant emotion, that troubled the excitement and perplexity of his heart, was fear, fear of that which he saw. There was about her the same manner, the same intonation in her voice, now as then, but she was not what he had known her to be. He knew quite well what she had been for him. And gradually he was realising that she was something quite other, and always had been.

She put no covering on her head, merely took off her apron, saying, 'We will go by the larches.' As they passed the old orchard, she called him in to show him a blue-tit's nest in one of the apple trees, and a sycock's in the hedge. He rather wondered at her surety, at a certain hardness like arrogance hidden under her humility.

'Look at the apple buds,' she said, and he then perceived myriads of little scarlet balls among the drooping boughs. Watching his face, her eyes went hard. She saw the scales were fallen from him, and at last he was going to see her as she was. It was the thing she had most dreaded in the past, and most needed, for her soul's sake. Now he was going to see her as she was. He would not love her, and he would know he never could have loved her. The old illusion gone, they were strangers, crude and entire. But he would give her her due – she would have her due from him.

She was brilliant as he had not known her. She showed him nests: a jenny wren's in a low bush.

'See this jinty's!' she exclaimed.

He was surprised to hear her use the local name. She reached carefully through the thorns, and put her fingers in the nest's round door.

'Five!' she said. 'Tiny little things.'

She showed him nests of robins, and chaffinches, and linnets, and buntings; of a wagtail beside the water.

'And if we go down, nearer the lake, I will show you a kingfisher's . . .'

'Among the young fir trees,' she said, 'there's a throstle's or a blackie's on nearly every bough, every ledge. The first day, when I had seen them all, I felt as if I mustn't go in the wood. It seemed a city of birds: and in the morning, hearing them all, I thought of the noisy early markets. I was afraid to go in my own wood.'

She was using the language they had both of them invented. Now it was all her own. He had done with it. She did not mind his silence, but was always dominant, letting him see her wood. As they came along a marshy path where forget-me-nots were opening in a rich blue drift: 'We know all the birds, but there are many flowers we can't find out,' she said. It was half an appeal to him, who had known the names of things.

She looked dreamily across to the open fields that slept in the sun.

'I have a lover as well, you know,' she said, with assurance, yet dropping again almost into the intimate tone.

This woke in him the spirit to fight her.

'I think I met him. He is good-looking – also in Arcady.'

Without answering, she turned into a dark path that led uphill, where the trees and undergrowth were very thick.

'They did well,' she said at length, 'to have various altars to various gods, in old days.'

'Ah yes!' he agreed. 'To whom is the new one?'

'There are no old ones,' she said. 'I was always looking for this.'

'And whose is it?' he asked.

'I don't know,' she said, looking full at him.

'I'm very glad, for your sake,' he said, 'that you are satisfied.'

'Aye – but the man doesn't matter so much,' she said. There was a pause.

'No!' he exclaimed, astonished, yet recognising her as her real self.

'It is one's self that matters,' she said. 'Whether one is being one's own self and serving one's own God.'

There was silence, during which he pondered. The path was almost flowerless, gloomy. At the side, his heels sank into soft clay.

III

'I,' she said, very slowly, 'I was married the same night as you.'

He looked at her.

'Not legally, of course,' she replied. 'But – actually.'

'To the keeper?' he said, not knowing what else to say.

She turned to him.

'You thought I could not?' she said. But the flush was deep in her cheek and throat, for all her assurance.

Still he would not say anything.

'You see' – she was making an effort to explain – '*I* had to understand also.'

'And what does it amount to, this *understanding*?' he asked.

'A very great deal – does it not to you?' she replied. 'One is free.'

'And you are not disappointed?'

'Far from it!' Her tone was deep and sincere.

'You love him?'

'Yes, I love him.'

'Good!' he said.

This silenced her for a while.

'Here, among his things, I love him,' she said.

His conceit would not let him be silent.

'It needs this setting?' he asked.

'It does,' she cried. 'You were always making me to be not myself.'

He laughed shortly.

'But is it a matter of surroundings?' he said. He had considered her all spirit.

'I am like a plant,' she replied. 'I can only grow in my own soil.'

They came to a place where the undergrowth shrank away, leaving a bare, brown space, pillared with the brick-red and purplish trunks of pine trees. On the fringe, hung the sombre green of elder trees, with flat flowers in bud, and below were bright, unfurling pennons of fern. In the midst of the bare space stood a keeper's log hut. Pheasant-coops were lying about, some occupied by a clucking hen, some empty.

Hilda walked over the brown pine-needles to the hut, took a key from among the eaves, and opened the door. It was a bare wooden place with a carpenter's bench and form, carpenter's tools, an axe, snares, straps, some skins pegged down, everything in order. Hilda closed the door. Syson examined the weird flat coats of wild animals, that were pegged down to be cured. She turned some knotch in the side wall, and disclosed a second, small apartment.

'How romantic!' said Syson.

'Yes. He is very curious – he has some of a wild animal's cunning – in a nice sense – and he is inventive, and thoughtful – but not beyond a certain point.'

She pulled back a dark green curtain. The apartment was occupied almost entirely by a large couch of heather and bracken, on which was spread an ample rabbit-skin rug. On the floor were patchwork rugs of cat-skin, and a red calf-skin, while hanging from the wall were other furs. Hilda took down one, which she put on. It was a cloak of rabbit-skin and of white fur, with a hood, apparently of the skins of stoats. She laughed at Syson from out of this barbaric mantle, saying:

'What do you think of it?'

'Ah –! I congratulate you on your man,' he replied.

'And look!' she said.

In a little jar on a shelf were some sprays, frail and white, of the first honeysuckle.

'They will scent the place at night,' she said.

He looked round curiously.

'Where does he come short, then?' he asked. She gazed at him for a few moments. Then, turning aside:

'The stars aren't the same with him,' she said. 'You could make them flash and quiver, and the forget-me-nots come up at me like phosphorescence. You could make things *wonderful*. I have found it out – it is true. But I have them all for myself, now.'

He laughed, saying:

'After all, stars and forget-me-nots are only luxuries. You ought to make poetry.'

'Aye,' she assented. 'But I have them all now.'

Again he laughed bitterly at her.

She turned swiftly. He was leaning against the small window of the tiny, obscure room, and was watching her, who stood in the doorway, still cloaked in her mantle. His cap was removed, so she saw his face and head distinctly in the dim room. His black, straight, glossy hair was brushed clean back from his brow. His black eyes were watching her, and his face, that was clear and cream, and perfectly smooth, was flickering.

'We are very different,' she said bitterly.

Again he laughed.

'I see you disapprove of me,' he said.

'I disapprove of what you have become,' she said.

'You think we might' – he glanced at the hut – 'have been like this – you and I?'

She shook her head.

'You! no; never! You plucked a thing and looked at it till you had found out all you wanted to know about it, then you threw it away,' she said.

'Did I?' he asked. 'And could your way never have been my way? I suppose not.'

'Why should it?' she said. 'I am a separate being.'

'But surely two people sometimes go the same way,' he said.

'You took me away from myself,' she said.

He knew he had mistaken her, had taken her for something she was not. That was his fault, not hers.

'And did you always know?' he asked.

'No – you never let me know. You bullied me. I couldn't help myself. I was glad when you left me, really.'

'I know you were,' he said. But his face went paler, almost deathly luminous.

'Yet,' he said, 'it was you who sent me the way I have gone.'

'I!' she exclaimed, in pride.

'You *would* have me take the Grammar School scholarship – and you would have me foster poor little Botell's fervent attachment to me, till he couldn't live without me – and because Botell was rich and influential. You triumphed in the wine-merchant's offer to send me to Cambridge, to befriend his only child. You wanted me to rise in the world. And all the time you were sending me away from you – every new success of mine put a separation between us, and more for you than for me. You never wanted to come with me: you wanted just to send me to see what it was like. I believe you even wanted me to marry a lady. You wanted to triumph over society in me.'

'And I am responsible,' she said, with sarcasm.

'I distinguished myself to satisfy you,' he replied.

'Ah!' she cried, 'you always wanted change, change, like a child.'

'Very well! And I am a success, and I know it, and I do some good work. But – I thought you were different. What right have you to a man?'

'What do you want?' she said, looking at him with wide, fearful eyes.

He looked back at her, his eyes pointed, like weapons.

'Why, nothing,' he laughed shortly.

There was a rattling at the outer latch, and the keeper entered. The woman glanced round, but remained standing, fur-cloaked, in the inner doorway. Syson did not move.

The other man entered, saw, and turned away without speaking. The two also were silent.

Pilbeam attended to his skins.

'I must go,' said Syson.

'Yes,' she replied.

'Then I give you "To our vast and varying fortunes."' He lifted his hand in pledge.

'"To our vast and varying fortunes,"' she answered gravely, and speaking in cold tones.

'Arthur!' she said.

The keeper pretended not to hear. Syson, watching keenly, began to smile. The woman drew herself up.

'Arthur!' she said again, with a curious upward inflection, which warned the two men that her soul was trembling on a dangerous crisis.

The keeper slowly put down his tool and came to her.

'Yes,' he said.

'I wanted to introduce you,' she said, trembling.

'I've met him a'ready,' said the keeper.

'Have you? It is Addy, Mr Syson, whom you know about. – This is Arthur, Mr Pilbeam,' she added, turning to Syson. The latter held out his hand to the keeper, and they shook hands in silence.

'I'm glad to have met you,' said Syson. 'We drop our correspondence, Hilda?'

'Why need we?' she asked.

The two men stood at a loss.

'*Is* there no need?' said Syson.

Still she was silent.

'It is as you will,' she said.

They went all three together down the gloomy path.

'"Qu'il était bleu, le ciel, et grand l'espoir,"' quoted Syson, not knowing what to say.

'What do you mean?' she said. 'Beside, *we* can't walk in *our* wild oats – we never sowed any.'

Syson looked at her. He was startled to see his young love, his nun, his Botticelli angel, so revealed. It was he who had been the fool. He and she were more separate than any two strangers could be. She only wanted to keep up a correspondence with him – and he, of course, wanted it kept up, so that he could write to her, like Dante to some Beatrice who had never existed save in the man's own brain.

At the bottom of the path she left him. He went along with the keeper, towards the open, towards the gate that closed on the wood. The two men walked almost like friends. They did not broach the subject of their thoughts.

Instead of going straight to the high-road gate, Syson went along the wood's edge, where the brook spread out in a little bog, and under the alder trees, among the reeds, great yellow stools and bosses of marigolds shone. Threads of brown water trickled by, touched with gold from the flowers. Suddenly there was a blue flash in the air, as a kingfisher passed.

Syson was extraordinarily moved. He climbed the bank to the gorse bushes, whose sparks of blossom had not yet gathered into a flame. Lying on the dry brown turf, he discovered sprigs of tiny purple milkwort and pink spots of lousewort. What a wonderful world it was – marvellous, for ever new. He felt as if it were underground, like the fields of monotone hell, notwithstanding. Inside his breast was a pain like a wound. He remembered the poem of William Morris, where in the Chapel of Lyonesse a knight lay wounded, with the truncheon of a spear deep in his breast, lying always as dead, yet did not die, while day after day the coloured sunlight dipped from the painted window across the chancel, and passed away. He knew now it never had been true, that which was between him and her, not for a moment. The truth had stood apart all the time.

Syson turned over. The air was full of the sound of larks, as if the sunshine above were condensing and falling in a shower. Amid this bright sound, voices sounded small and distinct.

'But if he's married, an' quite willing to drop it off, what has ter against it?' said the man's voice.

'I don't want to talk about it now. I want to be alone.'

Syson looked through the bushes. Hilda was standing in the wood, near the gate. The man was in the field, loitering by the hedge, and playing with the bees as they settled on the white bramble flowers.

There was silence for a while, in which Syson imagined her will among the brightness of the larks. Suddenly the keeper exclaimed 'Ah!' and swore. He was gripping at the sleeve of his coat, near the shoulder. Then he pulled off his jacket, threw it on the ground, and absorbedly rolled up his shirt sleeve right to the shoulder.

'Ah!' he said vindictively, as he picked out the bee and flung it away. He twisted his fine, bright arm, peering awkwardly over his shoulder.

'What is it?' asked Hilda.

'A bee – crawled up my sleeve,' he answered.

'Come here to me,' she said.

The keeper went to her, like a sulky boy. She took his arm in her hands.

'Here it is – and the sting left in – poor bee!'

She picked out the sting, put her mouth to his arm, and sucked away the drop of poison. As she looked at the red mark her mouth had made, and at his arm, she said, laughing:

'That is the reddest kiss you will ever have.'

When Syson next looked up, at the sound of voices, he saw in the shadow the keeper with his mouth on the throat of his beloved, whose head was thrown back, and whose hair had fallen, so that one rough rope of dark brown hair hung across his bare arm.

'No,' the woman answered. 'I am not upset because he's gone. You won't understand ...'

Syson could not distinguish what the man said. Hilda replied, clear and distinct:

'You know I love you. He has gone quite out of my life – don't trouble about him ...' He kissed her, murmuring. She laughed hollowly.

'Yes,' she said, indulgent. 'We will be married, we will be married. But not just yet.' He spoke to her again. Syson heard nothing for a time. Then she said:

'You must go home, now, dear – you will get no sleep.'

Again was heard the murmur of the keeper's voice, troubled by fear and passion.

'But why should we be married at once?' she said. 'What more would you have, by being married? It is most beautiful as it is.'

At last he pulled on his coat and departed. She stood at the gate, not watching him, but looking over the sunny country.

When at last she had gone, Syson also departed, going back to town.

Second Best

'Oh, I'm tired!' Frances exclaimed petulantly, and in the same instant she dropped down on the turf, near the hedge-bottom. Anne stood a moment surprised, then, accustomed to the vagaries of her beloved Frances, said:

'Well, and aren't you always likely to be tired, after travelling that blessed long way from Liverpool yesterday?' and she plumped down beside her sister. Anne was a wise young body of fourteen, very buxom, brimming with common sense. Frances was much older, about twenty-three, and whimsical, spasmodic. She was the beauty and the clever child of the family. She plucked the goose-grass buttons from her dress in a nervous, desperate fashion. Her beautiful profile, looped above with black hair, warm with the dusky-and-scarlet complexion of a pear, was calm as a mask, her thin brown hand plucked nervously.

'It's not the journey,' she said, objecting to Anne's obtuseness. Anne looked inquiringly at her darling. The young girl, in her self-confident, practical way, proceeded to reckon up this whimsical creature. But suddenly she found herself full in the eyes of Frances; felt two dark, hectic eyes flaring challenge at her, and she shrank away. Frances was peculiar for these great, exposed looks, which disconcerted people by their violence and their suddenness.

'What's a matter, poor old duck?' asked Anne, as she folded the slight, wilful form of her sister in her arms. Frances laughed shakily, and nestled down for comfort on the budding breasts of the strong girl.

'Oh, I'm only a bit tired,' she murmured, on the point of tears.

'Well, of course you are, what do you expect?' soothed Anne. It was a joke to Frances that Anne should play elder, almost mother to her. But then, Anne was in her unvexed teens; men were like big dogs to her: while Frances, at twenty-three, suffered a good deal.

The country was intensely morning-still. On the common everything shone beside its shadow, and the hillside gave off heat in silence. The brown turf seemed in a low state of combustion, the leaves of the oaks were scorched brown. Among the blackish foliage in the distance shone the small red and orange of the village.

The willows in the brook-course at the foot of the common suddenly shook with a dazzling effect like diamonds. It was a puff of wind. Anne resumed her normal position. She spread her knees, and put in her lap a handful of hazel nuts, whity-green leafy things, whose one cheek was tanned between brown and pink. These she began to crack and eat. Frances, with bowed head, mused bitterly.

'Eh, you know Tom Smedley?' began the young girl, as she pulled a tight kernel out of its shell.

'I suppose so,' replied Frances sarcastically.

'Well, he gave me a wild rabbit what he'd caught, to keep with my tame one – and it's living.'

'That's a good thing,' said Frances, very detached and ironic.

'Well, it *is*! He reckoned he'd take me to Ollerton Feast, but he never did. Look here, he took a servant from the rectory; I saw him.'

'So he ought,' said Frances.

'No, he oughtn't! and I told him so. And I told him I should tell you – an' I have done.'

Click and snap went a nut between her teeth. She sorted out the kernel, and chewed complacently.

'It doesn't make much difference,' said Frances.

'Well, 'appen it doesn't; but I was mad with him all the same.'

'Why?'

'Because I was; he's no right to go with a servant.'

'He's a perfect right,' persisted Frances, very just and cold.

'No, he hasn't, when he'd said he'd take me.'

Frances burst into a laugh of amusement and relief.

'Oh, no; I'd forgot that,' she said, adding, 'And what did he say when you promised to tell me?'

'He laughed and said, "She won't fret her fat over that."'

'And she won't,' sniffed Frances.

There was silence. The common, with its sere, blonde-headed thistles, its heaps of silent bramble, its brown-husked gorse in the glare of sunshine, seemed visionary. Across the brook began the immense pattern of agriculture, white chequering of barley stubble, brown squares of wheat, khaki patches of pasture, red stripes of fallow, with the woodland and the tiny village dark like ornaments, leading away to the distance, right to the hills, where the check-pattern grew smaller and smaller, till, in the blackish haze of heat, far off, only the tiny white squares of barley stubble showed distinct.

'Eh, I say, here's a rabbit hole!' cried Anne suddenly. 'Should we watch if one comes out? You won't have to fidget, you know.'

The two girls sat perfectly still. Frances watched certain objects in her surroundings: they had a peculiar, unfriendly look about them: the weight of greenish elderberries on their purpling stalks; the twinkling of the yellowing crab-apples that clustered high up in the hedge, against the sky: the exhausted, limp leaves of the primroses lying flat in the hedge-bottom: all looked strange to her. Then her eyes caught a movement. A mole was moving silently over the warm, red soil, nosing, shuffling hither and thither, flat, and dark as a shadow, shifting about, and as suddenly brisk, and as silent, like a very ghost of *joie de vivre.* Frances started, from habit was about to call on Anne to kill the little pest. But, to-day, her lethargy of unhappiness was too much for her. She watched the little brute paddling, snuffing, touching things to discover them, running in blindness, delighted to ecstasy by the sunlight and the hot, strange things that caressed its belly and its nose. She felt a keen pity for the little creature.

'Eh, our Fran, look there! It's a mole.'

Anne was on her feet, standing watching the dark, unconscious beast. Frances frowned with anxiety.

'It doesn't run off, does it?' said the young girl softly. Then she stealthily approached the creature. The mole paddled fumblingly away. In an instant Anne put her foot upon it, not too heavily. Frances could see the struggling, swimming movement of the little pink hands of the brute, the twisting and twitching of its pointed nose, as it wrestled under the sole of the boot.

'It *does* wriggle!' said the bonny girl, knitting her brows in a frown at the eerie sensation. Then she bent down to look at her trap. Frances could now see, beyond the edge of the boot-sole, the heaving of the velvet shoulders, the pitiful turning of the sightless face, the frantic rowing of the flat, pink hands.

'Kill the thing,' she said, turning away her face.

'Oh – I'm not,' laughed Anne, shrinking. 'You can, if you like.'

'I *don't* like,' said Frances, with quiet intensity.

After several dabbling attempts, Anne succeeded in picking up the little animal by the scruff of its neck. It threw back its head, flung its long blind snout from side to side, the mouth open in a peculiar oblong, with tiny pinkish teeth at the edge. The blind, frantic mouth gaped and writhed. The body, heavy and clumsy, hung scarcely moving.

'Isn't it a snappy little thing,' observed Anne twisting to avoid the teeth.

'What are you going to do with it?' asked Frances sharply.

'It's got to be killed – look at the damage they do. I s'll take it home and let dadda or somebody kill it. I'm not going to let it go.'

She swaddled the creature clumsily in her pocket-handkerchief and sat down beside her sister. There was an interval of silence, during which Anne combated the efforts of the mole.

'You've not had much to say about Jimmy this time. Did you see him often in Liverpool?' Anne asked suddenly.

'Once or twice,' replied Frances, giving no sign of how the question troubled her.

'And aren't you sweet on him any more, then?'

'I should think I'm not, seeing that he's engaged.'

'Engaged? Jimmy Barrass! Well, of all things! I never thought *he'd* get engaged.'

'Why not, he's as much right as anybody else?' snapped Frances.

Anne was fumbling with the mole.

''Appen so,' she said at length; 'but I never thought Jimmy would, though.'

'Why not?' snapped Frances.

'*I* don't know – this blessed mole, it'll not keep still! – who's he got engaged to?'

'How should I know?'

'I thought you'd ask him; you've known him long enough. I s'd think he thought he'd get engaged now he's a Doctor of Chemistry.'

Frances laughed in spite of herself.

'What's that got to do with it?' she asked.

'I'm sure it's got a lot: He'll want to feel *somebody* now, so he's got engaged. Hey, stop it; go in!'

But at this juncture the mole almost succeeded in wriggling clear. It wrestled and twisted frantically, waved its pointed blind head, its mouth standing open like a little shaft, its big, wrinkled hands spread out.

'Go in with you!' urged Anne, poking the little creature with her forefinger, trying to get it back into the handkerchief. Suddenly the mouth turned like a spark on her finger.

'Oh!' she cried, 'he's bit me.'

She dropped him to the floor. Dazed, the blind creature fumbled round. Frances felt like shrieking. She expected him to dart away in a flash, like a mouse, and there he remained groping; she wanted to cry to him to be gone. Anne, in a sudden decision of wrath, caught up her sister's walking-cane. With one blow the mole was dead. Frances was startled and shocked. One moment the little wretch was fussing in the heat, and the next it lay like a little bag, inert and black – not a struggle, scarce a quiver.

'It is dead!' Frances said breathlessly. Anne took her finger from her mouth, looked at the tiny pinpricks, and said:

'Yes, he is, and I'm glad. They're vicious little nuisances, moles are.'

With which her wrath vanished. She picked up the dead animal.

'Hasn't it got a beautiful skin,' she mused, stroking the fur with her forefinger, then with her check.

'Mind,' said Frances sharply. 'You'll have the blood on your skirt!'

One ruby drop of blood hung on the small snout, ready to fall. Anne shook it off on to some harebells. Frances suddenly became calm; in that moment, grown-up.

'I suppose they have to be killed,' she said, and a certain rather dreary indifference succeeded to her grief. The twinkling crab-apples, the glitter of brilliant willows now seemed to her trifling, scarcely worth the notice. Something had died in her, so that things lost their poignancy. She was calm, indifference overlying her quiet sadness. Rising, she walked down to the brook course.

'Here, wait for me,' cried Anne, coming tumbling after.

Frances stood on the bridge, looking at the red mud trodden into pockets by the feet of cattle. There was not a drain of water left, but everything smelled green, succulent. Why did she care so little for Anne, who was so fond of her? she asked herself. Why did she care so little for anyone? She did not know, but she felt a rather stubborn pride in her isolation and indifference.

They entered a field where stooks of barley stood in rows,

the straight, blonde tresses of the corn streaming on to the ground. The stubble was bleached by the intense summer, so that the expanse glared white. The next field was sweet and soft with a second crop of seeds; thin, straggling clover whose little pink knobs rested prettily in the dark green. The scent was faint and sickly. The girls came up in single file, Frances leading.

Near the gate a young man was mowing with the scythe some fodder for the afternoon feed of the cattle. As he saw the girls he left off working and waited in an aimless kind of way. Frances was dressed in white muslin, and she walked with dignity, detached and forgetful. Her lack of agitation, her simple, unheeding advance made him nervous. She had loved the far-off Jimmy for five years, having had in return his half-measures. This man only affected her slightly.

Tom was of medium stature, energetic in build. His smooth, fair-skinned face was burned red, not brown, by the sun, and this ruddiness enhanced his appearance of good humour and easiness. Being a year older than Frances, he would have courted her long ago had she been so inclined. As it was, he had gone his uneventful way amiably, chatting with many a girl, but remaining unattached, free of trouble for the most part. Only he knew he wanted a woman. He hitched his trousers just a trifle self-consciously as the girls approached. Frances was a rare, delicate kind of being, whom he realised with a queer and delicious stimulation in his veins. She gave him a slight sense of suffocation. Somehow, this morning, she affected him more than usual. She was dressed in white. He, however, being matter-of-fact in his mind, did not realise. His feeling had never become conscious, purposive.

Frances knew what she was about. Tom was ready to love her as soon as she would show him. Now that she could not have Jimmy, she did not poignantly care. Still, she would have something. If she could not have the best – Jimmy, whom she knew to be something of a snob – she would have the second best, Tom. She advanced rather indifferently.

'You are back, then!' said Tom. She marked the touch of uncertainty in his voice.

'No,' she laughed, 'I'm still in Liverpool,' and the undertone of intimacy made him burn.

'This isn't you, then?' he asked.

Her heart leapt up in approval. She looked in his eyes, and for a second was with him.

'Why, what do you think?' she laughed.

He lifted his hat from his head with a distracted little gesture. She liked him, his quaint ways, his humour, his ignorance, and his slow masculinity.

'Here, look here, Tom Smedley,' broke in Anne.

'A moudiwarp! Did you find it dead?' he asked.

'No, it bit me,' said Anne.

'Oh, aye! An' that got your rag out, did it?'

'No, it didn't!' Anne scolded sharply. 'Such language!'

'Oh, what's up wi' it?'

'I can't bear you to talk broad.'

'Can't you?'

He glanced at Frances.

'It isn't nice,' Frances said. She did not care, really. The vulgar speech jarred on her as a rule; Jimmy was a gentleman. But Tom's manner of speech did not matter to her.

'I like you to talk *nicely*,' she added.

'Do you,' he replied, tilting his hat, stirred.

'And generally you *do*, you know,' she smiled.

'I s'll have to have a try,' he said, rather tensely gallant.

'What?' she asked brightly.

'To talk nice to you,' he said. Frances coloured furiously, bent her head for a moment, then laughed gaily, as if she liked this clumsy hint.

'Eh now, you mind what you're saying,' cried Anne, giving the young man an admonitory pat.

'You wouldn't have to give yon mole many knocks like that,' he teased, relieved to get on safe ground, rubbing his arm.

'No indeed, it died in one blow,' said Frances, with a flippancy that was hateful to her.

'You're not so good at knockin' 'em?' he said, turning to her.

'I don't know, if I'm cross,' she said decisively.

'No?' he replied, with alert attentiveness.

'I could,' she added, harder, 'if it was necessary.'

He was slow to feel her difference.

'And don't you consider it *is* necessary?' he asked, with misgiving.

'W – ell – is it?' she said, looking at him steadily, coldly.

'I reckon it is,' he replied, looking away, but standing stubborn.

She laughed quickly.

'But it isn't necessary for *me,*' she said, with slight contempt.

'Yes, that's quite true,' he answered.

She laughed in a shaky fashion.

'*I know it is,*' she said; and there was an awkward pause.

'Why, would you *like* me to kill moles then?' she asked tentatively, after a while.

'They do us a lot of damage,' he said, standing firm on his own ground, angered.

'Well, I'll see the next time I come across one,' she promised, defiantly. Their eyes met, and she sank before him, her pride troubled. He felt uneasy and triumphant and baffled, as if fate had gripped him. She smiled as she departed.

'Well,' said Anne, as the sisters went through the wheat stubble; 'I don't know what you two's been jawing about, I'm sure.'

'Don't you?' laughed Frances significantly.

'No, I don't. But, at any rate, Tom Smedley's a good deal better to my thinking than Jimmy, so there – and nicer.'

'Perhaps he is,' said Frances coldly.

And the next day, after a secret, persistent hunt, she found another mole playing in the heat. She killed it, and in the evening, when Tom came to the gate to smoke his pipe after supper, she took him the dead creature.

'Here you are then!' she said.

'Did you catch it?' he replied, taking the velvet corpse into his fingers and examining it minutely. This was to hide his trepidation.

'Did you think I couldn't?' she asked, her face very near his.

'Nay, I didn't know.'

She laughed in his face, a strange little laugh that caught her breath, all agitation, and tears, and recklessness of desire. He looked frightened and upset. She put her hand to his arm.

'Shall you go out wi' me?' he asked, in a difficult, troubled tone.

She turned her face away, with a shaky laugh. The blood came up in him, strong, overmastering. He resisted it. But it drove him down, and he was carried away. Seeing the winsome, frail nape of her neck, fierce love came upon him for her, and tenderness.

'We s'll 'ave to tell your mother,' he said. And he stood, suffering, resisting his passion for her.

'Yes,' she replied, in a dead voice. But there was a thrill of pleasure in this death.

Her Turn

She was his second wife, and so there was between them that truce which is never held between a man and his first wife.

He was one for the women, and as such, an exception among the colliers. In spite of their prudery the neighbour women liked him; he was big, naïve, and very courteous with them, as he was even with his second wife.

Being a large man of considerable strength and perfect health, he earned good money in the pit. His natural courtesy saved him from enemies, while his good humour made him always welcome. So he went his own way, had plenty of friends, a good job down pit.

He gave his wife thirty-five shillings a week. He had two grown-up sons at home, and they paid twelve shillings each. There was only one child by the second marriage, so Radford considered his wife did well.

Eighteen months ago, Bryan and Wentworth's men were out on strike for eleven weeks. During that time, Mrs Radford could neither cajole not entreat nor nag the eleven shillings strike-pay from her husband. So that when the second strike came on, she was prepared for action.

Radford was going, quite inconspicuously, to the publican's wife at the 'Golden Horn'. She is a large, easy-going lady of forty, and her husband is sixty-three, moreover crippled with rheumatism. She sits in the little bar-parlour of the wayside public-house, knitting for dear life, and sipping a moderate glass of Scotch. When a decent man arrives at the three-foot width of bar, she rises, serves him, scans him over, and, if she likes his looks, says:

'Won't you step inside, sir?'

If he steps inside, he will find not more than one or two men present. The room is warm and quite small. The landlady knits. She gives a few polite words to the stranger, then resumes her conversation with the man most important to her. She is straight, highly coloured, with indifferent brown eyes.

'What was that you asked me, Mr Radford?'

'What is the difference between a donkey's tail and a rainbow?' asked Radford, who had a consuming passion for conundrums.

'All the difference in the world,' replied the landlady.

'Yes, but what special difference?'

'I s'll have to give it up again. You'll think me a donkey's head, I'm afraid.'

'Not likely. But just you consider now, wheer . . .'

The conundrum was still under weigh, when a girl entered. She was swarthy, a fine animal. After she had gone out:

'Do you know who that is?' asked the landlady.

'I can't say as I do,' replied Radford.

'She's Frederick Pinnock's daughter, from Stony Ford. She's courting our Willy.'

'And a fine lass, too.'

'Yes, fine enough, as far as that goes. What sort of a wife'll she make him, think you?'

'You just let me consider a bit,' said the man. He took out a pocket-book and a pencil. The landlady continued to talk to the other guests.

Radford was a big fellow, black-haired, with a brown moustache, and darkish blue eyes. His voice, naturally deep, was pitched in his throat, and had a peculiar tenor quality, rather husky, and disturbing. He modulated it a good deal as he spoke, as men do who talk much with women. Always there was a certain indolence in his carriage.

'Our mester's lazy,' his wife said of him. 'There's many a bit of a job wants doin,' but get him to do it if you can.'

But she knew he was merely indifferent to the little jobs, and not lazy.

He sat writing for about ten minutes, at the end of which time he read:

'I see a fine girl full of life

I see her just ready for wedlock,
But there's jealousy between her eyebrows
And jealousy on her mouth.
I see trouble ahead
Willy is delicate.
She would do him no good.
She would have no thought for his ailment.
She would only see what she wanted –'

So in phrases, he got down his thoughts. He had to fumble for expression, and anything serious he wanted to say he wrote in 'poetry,' as he called it.

Presently, the landlady rose, saying:

'Well, I s'll have to be looking after our mester. I s'll be in again before we close.'

Radford sat quite comfortably on. In a while he too bade the company good-night.

When he got home, at a quarter-past eleven, his sons were in bed, and his wife sat awaiting him. She was a woman of medium height, fat, and sleek, a dumpling. Her black hair was parted smooth, her narrow-opened eyes were sly and satirical; she had a peculiar twang in her rather sleering voice.

'Our missis is a puss-puss,' he said easily, of her. Her extraordinarily smooth, sleek face was remarkable. She was very healthy.

He never came in drunk. Having taken off his coat and his cap, he sat down to supper in his shirt-sleeves. Do as he might, she was fascinated by him. He had a strong neck, with the crisp hair growing low. Let her be angry as she would, yet she had a passion for that neck of his, particularly when she saw the great vein rib under the skin.

'I think, missis,' he said, 'I'd rather ha'e a smite o' cheese than this meat.'

'Well, can't you get it yourself?'

'Yi, surely I can,' he said, and went out to the pantry.

'I think if yer comin' in at this time of night you can wait on yourself,' she justified herself.

She moved uneasily in her chair. There were several jam tarts alongside the cheese on the dish he brought.

'Yi, Missis, them tan-tafflins 'll go down very nicely,' he said.

'Oh, will they! Then you'd better help to pay for them,' she said, suavely.

'Now what art after?'

'What am I after? Why, can't you think?' she said sarcastically.

'I'm not for thinkin,' this hour, Missis.'

'No, I know you're not. But wheer's my money? You've been paid th' Union to-day. Wheer do I come in?'

'Tha's got money, an' tha mun use it.'

'Thank yer. An' 'aven't you none, as well?'

'I hadna, not till we was paid, not a ha'ep'ny.'

'Then you ought to be ashamed of yourself to say so.'

''Appen so!'

'We'll go shares wi' th' Union money,' she said. 'That's nothing but what's right.'

'We shonna. Tha's got plenty o' money as tha can use.'

'Oh, all right,' she cried. 'I will do.'

She went to bed. It made her feel sharp that she could not get at him.

The next day she was just as usual. But at eleven o'clock she took her purse and went up-town. Trade was very slack. Men stood about in gangs, men were playing marbles everywhere in the streets. It was a sunny morning. Mrs Radford went into the furnisher-and-upholsterer's shop.

'There's a few things,' she said to Mr Allcock, 'as I'm wantin' for the house, and I might as well get them now, while the men's at home, and can shift me the furniture.'

She put her fat purse on to the counter with a click. The man should know she was not wanting 'strap'. She bought linoleum for the kitchen, a new wringer, a breakfast service, a spring mattress, and various other things, keeping a mere thirty shillings, which she tied in a corner of her handkerchief. In her purse was some loose silver.

Her husband was gardening in a desultory fashion when she got back home. The daffodils were out. The colts in the field at the end of the garden were tossing their velvety brown necks.

'Sithee here, Missis,' called Radford, from the shed which stood half-way down the path. Two doves in a cage were cooing.

'What have you got?' asked the woman as she approached. He held out to her in his big earthy hand a tortoise. The reptile was very, very slowly issuing its head again to the warmth.

'He's wakkened up betimes,' said Radford.

'He's like th' men, wakened up for a holiday,' said the wife. Radford scratched the little beast's scaley head.

'We pleased to see him out,' he said.

They had just finished dinner, when a man knocked at the door.

'From Allcock's!' he said.

The plump woman took up the clothes-basket containing the crockery she had bought.

'Whativer hast got theer?' asked her husband.

'We've been wantin' some breakfast cups for ages, so I went up-town an' got 'em this mornin',' she replied.

He watched her taking out the crockery.

'Hm!' he said. 'Tha's been on th' spend, seemly!'

Again there was a thud at the door. The man had put down a roll of linoleum. Mr Radford went to look at it.

'They come rolling in!' he exclaimed.

'Who's grumbled more than you about the raggy oilcloth of this kitchen?' sang the insidious cat-like voice of the wife.

'It's all right; it's all right,' said Radford. The carter came up the entry carrying another roll, which he deposited with a grunt at the door.

'An' how much do you reckon this lot is?' asked Radford.

'Oh, they're all paid for, don't yer worry,' replied the wife.

'Shall yer gie' me a hand, Mester?' asked the carter.

Radford followed him down the entry, in his easy, slouching way. His wife went after. His waistcoat was hanging loose over his shirt. She watched his easy movement of well-being, as she followed him, and she laughed to herself. The carter took hold of one end of the wire mattress, dragged it forth.

'Well, this is a corker!' said Radford, as he received the burden. They walked with it up the entry.

'There's th' mangle!' said the carter.

'What dost reckon tha's been up to, Missis?' asked the husband.

'I said to myself last wash-day, if I had to turn that mangle again, tha'd ha'e ter wash the clothes thyself.'

Radford followed the carter down the entry again. In the street women were standing watching, and dozens of men were lounging round the cart. One officiously helped with the wringer.

'Gi'e him thrippence,' said Mrs Radford.

'Give 't him thy-sen,' replied her husband.

'I've no change under half-a-crown.'

Radford tipped the carter and returned indoors. He surveyed the array of crockery, linoleum, mattress, mangle, and other goods crowding the house and the yard.

'Well, this is a winder!' he repeated.

'We stood in need of 'em enough.'

'I hope tha's got plenty more from wheer they came from,' he replied dangerously.

'That's just what I haven't.' She opened her purse. 'Two half-crowns; that's ivery copper I've got i' th' world.'

He stood very still as he looked.

'It's right,' she said.

There was a certain smug sense of satisfaction about her. A wave of anger came over him, blinding him. But he waited and waited. Suddenly his arm leapt up, the fist clenched, and his eyes blazed at her. She shrank away, pale and frightened. But he dropped his fist to his side, turned, and went out muttering. He went down to the shed that stood in the middle of the garden. There he picked up the tortoise, and stood with bent head, rubbing its horny head.

She stood hesitating, watching him. Her heart was heavy, and yet there was a curious, cat-like look of satisfaction round her eyes. Then she went indoors and gazed at her new cups, admiringly.

The next week he handed her his half-sovereign without a word.

'You'll want some for yourself,' she said, and she gave him a shilling. He accepted it.

Tickets, Please

There is in the Midlands a single-line tramway system which boldly leaves the county town and plunges off into the black, industrial countryside, up hill and down dale, through the long ugly villages of workmen's houses, over canals and railways, past churches perched high and nobly over the smoke and shadows, through stark, grimy cold little market-places, tilting away in a rush past cinemas and shops down to the hollow where the collieries are, then up again, past a little rural church, under the ash trees, on in a rush to the terminus, the last little ugly place of industry, the cold little town that shivers on the edge of the wild, gloomy country beyond. There the green and creamy coloured tram-car seems to pause and purr with curious satisfaction. But in a few minutes – the clock on the turret of the Cooperative Wholesale Society's Shops gives the time – away it starts once more on the adventure. Again there are the reckless swoops downhill, bouncing the loops: again the chilly wait in the hill-top market-place: again the breathless slithering round the precipitous drop under the church: again the patient halts at the loops, waiting for the outcoming car: so on and on, for two long hours, till at last the city looms beyond the fat gas-works, the narrow factories draw near, we are in the sordid streets of the great town, once more we sidle to a standstill at our terminus, abashed by the great crimson and cream-coloured city cars, but still perky, jaunty, somewhat dare-devil, green as a jaunty sprig of parsley out of a black colliery garden.

To ride on these cars is always an adventure. Since we are in war-time, the drivers are men unfit for active service: cripples and hunchbacks. So they have the spirit of the devil in them. The ride becomes a steeplechase. Hurray! we have leapt in a clear jump over the canal bridges – now for the four-lane corner. With a shriek and a trail of sparks we are clear again. To be sure, a tram often leaps the rails – but what matter! It sits in a ditch till other trams come to haul it out. It is quite common for a car, packed with one solid mass of living people, to come to a dead halt in the midst of unbroken blackness, the heart of nowhere on a dark night, and for the driver and the girl conductor to call, 'All get off – car's on fire!' Instead, however, of rushing out in a panic, the passengers stolidly reply: 'Get on – get on! We're not coming out. We're stopping where we are. Push on, George.' So till flames actually appear.

The reason for this reluctance to dismount is that the nights are howlingly cold, black, and windswept, and a car is a haven of refuge. From village to village the miners travel, for a change of cinema, of girl, of pub. The trams are desperately packed. Who is going to risk himself in the black gulf outside, to wait perhaps an hour for another tram, then to see the forlorn notice 'Depot Only', because there is something wrong! Or to greet a unit of three bright cars all so tight with people that they sail past with a howl of derision. Trams that pass in the night.

This, the most dangerous tram-service in England, as the authorities themselves declare, with pride, is entirely conducted by girls, and driven by rash young men, a little crippled, or by delicate young men, who creep forward in terror. The girls are fearless young hussies. In their ugly blue uniform, skirts up to their knees, shapeless old peaked caps on their heads, they have all the *sang-froid* of an old non-commissioned officer. With a tram packed with howling colliers, roaring hymns downstairs and a sort of antiphony of obscenities upstairs, the lasses are perfectly at their ease. They pounce on the youths who try to evade their ticket-machine. They push off the men at the end of their distance. They are not going to be done in the eye – not they. They fear nobody – and everybody fears them.

'Hello, Annie!'

'Hello, Ted!'

'Oh, mind my corn, Miss Stone. It's my belief you've got a heart of stone, for you've trod on it again.'

'You should keep it in your pocket,' replies Miss Stone, and she goes sturdily upstairs in her high boots.

'Tickets, please.'

She is peremptory, suspicious, and ready to hit first. She can hold her own against ten thousand. The step of that tram-car is her Thermopylae.

Therefore, there is a certain wild romance aboard these cars – and in the sturdy bosom of Annie herself. The time for soft romance is in the morning, between ten o'clock and one, when things are rather slack: that is, except market-day and Saturday. Thus Annie has time to look about her. Then she often hops off her car and into a shop where she has spied something, while the driver chats in the main road. There is very good feeling between the girls and the drivers. Are they not companions in peril, shipmates aboard this careering vessel of a tram-car, for ever rocking on the waves of a stormy land.

Then, also, during the easy hours, the inspectors are most in evidence. For some reason, everybody employed in this tram-service is young: there are no grey heads. It would not do. Therefore the inspectors are of the right age, and one, the chief, is also good-looking. See him stand on a wet, gloomy morning, in his long oil-skin, his peaked cap well down over his eyes, waiting to board a car. His face is ruddy, his small brown moustache is weathered, he has a faint impudent smile. Fairly tall and agile, even in his waterproof, he springs aboard a car and greets Annie.

'Hello, Annie! Keeping the wet out?'

'Trying to.'

There are only two people in the car. Inspecting is soon over. Then for a long and impudent chat on the foot-board, a good, easy, twelve-mile chat.

The inspector's name is John Thomas Raynor – always called John Thomas, except sometimes, in malice, Coddy. His face sets in fury when he is addressed, from a distance, with this abbreviation. There is considerable scandal about John Thomas in half a dozen villages. He flirts with the girl conductors in the morning, and walks out with them in the dark night, when they leave their tram-car at the depot. Of course, the girls quit the service frequently. Then he flirts and walks out with the newcomer: always providing she is sufficiently attractive, and that she will consent to walk. It is remarkable, however, that most of the girls are quite comely, they are all young, and this roving life aboard the car gives them a sailor's dash and recklessness. What matter how they behave when the ship is in port. Tomorrow they will be aboard again.

Annie, however, was something of a Tartar, and her sharp tongue and kept John Thomas at arm's length for many months. Perhaps, therefore, she liked him all the more: for he always came up smiling, with impudence. She watched him vanquish one girl, then another. She could tell by the movement of his mouth and eyes, when he flirted with her in the morning, that he had been walking out with this lass, or the other, the night before. A fine cock-of-the-walk he was. She could sum him up pretty well.

In this subtle antagonism they knew each other like old friends, they were as shrewd with one another almost as man and wife. But Annie had always kept him sufficiently at arm's length. Besides, she had a boy of her own.

The Statutes fair, however, came in November, at Bestwood. It happened that Annie had the Monday night off. It was a drizzling ugly night, yet she dressed herself up and went to the fair ground. She was alone, but she expected soon to find a pal of some sort.

The roundabouts were veering round and grinding out their music, the side shows were making as much commotion as possible. In the cocoanut shies there were no cocoanuts, but artificial war-time substitutes, which the lads declared were fastened into the irons. There was a sad decline in brilliance and luxury. None the less, the ground was muddy as ever, there was the same crush, the press of faces lighted up by the flares and the electric lights, the same smell of naphtha and a few fried potatoes, and of electricity.

Who should be the first to greet Miss Annie on the show-ground but John Thomas. He had a black overcoat buttoned up to his chin, and a tweed cap pulled down over his brows, his face between was ruddy and smiling and handy as ever. She knew so well the way his mouth moved.

She was very glad to have a 'boy'. To be at the Statutes without a fellow was no fun. Instantly, like the gallant he was, he took her on the Dragons, grim-toothed, round-about switchbacks. It was not nearly so exciting as a tram-car actually. But, then, to be seated in a shaking, green dragon, uplifted above the sea of bubble faces, careering in a rickety fashion in the lower heavens, whilst John Thomas leaned over her, his cigarette in his mouth, was after all the right style. She was a plump, quick, alive little creature. So she was quite excited and happy.

John Thomas made her stay on for the next round. And therefore she could hardly for shame repulse him when he put his arm round her and drew her a little nearer to him, in a very warm and cuddly manner. Besides, he was fairly discreet, he kept his movement as hidden as possible. She looked down, and saw that his red, clean hand was out of sight of the crowd. And they knew each other so well. So they warmed up to the fair.

After the dragons they went on the horses. John Thomas paid each time, so she could but be complaisant. He, of course, sat astride on the outer horse – named 'Black Bess' – and she sat sideways, towards him, on the inner horse – named 'Wildfire'. But of course John Thomas was not going to sit discreetly on 'Black Bess', holding the brass bar. Round they spun and heaved, in the light. And round he swung on his wooden steed, flinging one leg across her mount, and perilously tipping up and down, across the space, half lying back, laughing at her. He was perfectly happy; she was afraid her hat was on one side, but she was excited.

He threw quoits on a table, and won for her two large, pale-blue hat-pins. And then, hearing the noise of the cinemas, announcing another performance, they climbed the boards and went in.

Of course, during these performances pitch darkness falls from time to time, when the machine goes wrong. Then there is a wild whooping, and a loud smacking of simulated kisses. In these moments John Thomas drew Annie towards him. After all, he had a wonderfully warm, cosy way of holding a girl with his arm, he seemed to make such a nice fit. And, after all, it was pleasant to be so held: so very comforting and cosy and nice. He leaned over her and she felt his breath on her hair; she knew he wanted to kiss her on the lips. And, after all, he was so warm and she fitted in to him so softly. After all, she wanted him to touch her lips.

But the light sprang up; she also started electrically, and put her hat straight. He left his arm lying nonchalantly behind her. Well, it was fun, it was exciting to be at the Statutes with John Thomas.

When the cinema was over they went for a walk across the dark, damp fields. He had all the arts of love-making. He was especially good at holding a girl, when he sat with her on a stile in the black, drizzling darkness. He seemed to be holding her in space, against his own warmth and gratification. And his kisses were soft and slow and searching.

So Annie walked out with John Thomas, though she kept her own boy dangling in the distance. Some of the tram-girls chose to be huffy. But there, you must take things as you find them, in this life.

There was no mistake about it, Annie liked John Thomas a good deal. She felt so rich and warm in herself whenever he was near. And John Thomas really liked Annie, more than usual. The soft, melting way in which she could flow into a fellow, as if she melted into his very bones, was something rare and good. He fully appreciated this.

But with a developing acquaintance there began a developing intimacy. Annie wanted to consider him a person, a man; she wanted to take an intelligent interest in him, and to have an intelligent response. She did not want a mere nocturnal presence, which was what he was so far. And she prided herself that he could not leave her.

Here she made a mistake. John Thomas intended to remain a nocturnal presence; he had no idea of becoming an all-round individual to her. When she started to take an intelligent interest in him and his life and his character, he sheered off. He hated intelligent interest. And he knew that the only way to stop it was to avoid it. The possessive female was aroused in Annie. So he left her.

It is no use saying she was not surprised. She was at first startled, thrown out of her count. For she had been so *very* sure of holding him. For a while she was staggered, and everything became uncertain to her. Then she wept with fury, indignation, desolation, and misery. Then she had a spasm of despair. And then, when he came, still impudently, on to her car, still familiar, but letting her see by the movement of his head that he had gone away to somebody else for the time being, and was enjoying pastures new, then she determined to have her own back.

She had a very shrewd idea what girls John Thomas had taken out. She went to Nora Purdy. Nora was a tall, rather pale, but well-built girl, with beautiful yellow hair. She was rather secretive.

'Hey!' said Annie, accosting her; then softly, 'Who's John Thomas on with now?'

'I don't know,' said Nora.

'Why tha does,' said Annie, ironically lapsing into dialect. 'Tha knows as well as I do.'

'Well, I do then,' said Nora. 'It isn't me, so don't bother.'

'It's Cissy Meakin, isn't it?'

'It is, for all I know.'

'Hasn't he got a face on him!' said Annie. 'I don't half like his cheek. I could knock him off the foot-board when he comes round at me.'

'He'll get dropped-on one of these days,' said Nora.

'Ay, he will, when somebody makes up their mind to drop it on him. I should like to see him taken down a peg or two, shouldn't you?'

'I shouldn't mind,' said Nora.

'You've got quite as much cause to as I have,' said Annie. 'But we'll drop on him one of these days, my girl. What? Don't you want to?'

'I don't mind,' said Nora.

But as a matter of fact, Nora was much more vindictive than Annie.

One by one Annie went the round of the old flames. It so happened that Cissy Meakin left the tramway service in quite a short time. Her mother made her leave. Then John Thomas was on the *qui-vive.* He cast his eyes over his old flock. And his eyes lighted on Annie. He thought she would be safe now. Besides, he liked her.

She arranged to walk home with him on Sunday night. It so happened that her car would be in the depot at half-past nine: the last car would come in at 10.15. So John Thomas was to wait for her there.

At the depot the girls had a little waiting-room of their own. It was quite rough, but cosy, with a fire and an oven and a mirror, and table and wooden chairs. The half dozen girls who knew John Thomas only too well had arranged to take service this Sunday afternoon. So, as the cars began to come in, early, the girls dropped into the waiting-room. And instead of hurrying off home, they sat around the fire and had a cup of tea. Outside was the darkness and lawlessness of war-time.

John Thomas came on the car after Annie, at about a quarter to ten. He poked his head easily into the girls' waiting-room.

'Prayer-meeting?' he asked.

'Ay,' said Laura Sharp. 'Ladies only.'

'That's me!' said John Thomas. It was one of his favourite exclamations.

'Shut the door, boy,' said Muriel Baggaley.

'On which side of me?' said John Thomas.

'Which tha likes,' said Polly Birkin.

He had come in and closed the door behind him. The girls moved in their circle, to make a place for him near the fire. He took off his great-coat and pushed back his hat.

'Who handles the teapot?' he said.

Nora Purdy silently poured him out a cup of tea.

'Want a bit o' my bread and drippin'?' said Muriel Baggaley to him.

'Ay, give us a bit.'

And he began to eat his piece of bread.

'There's no place like home, girls,' he said.

They all looked at him as he uttered this piece of impudence. He seemed to be sunning himself in the presence of so many damsels.

'Especially if you're not afraid to go home in the dark,' said Laura Sharp.

'Me! By myself I am.'

They sat till they heard the last tram come in. In a few minutes Emma Houselay entered.

'Come on, my old duck!' cried Polly Birkin.

'It *is* perishing,' said Emma, holding her fingers to the fire.

'But – I'm afraid to, go home in, the dark,' sang Laura Sharp, the tune having got into her mind.

'Who're you going with to-night, John Thomas?' asked Muriel Baggaley, coolly.

'To-night?' said John Thomas. 'Oh, I'm going home by myself to-night – all on my lonely-O.'

'That's me!' said Nora Purdy, using his own ejaculation.

The girls laughed shrilly.

'Me as well, Nora,' said John Thomas.

'Don't know what you mean,' said Laura.

'Yes, I'm toddling,' said he, rising and reaching for his overcoat.

'Nay,' said Polly. 'We're all here waiting for you.'

'We've got to be up in good time in the morning,' he said, in the benevolent official manner.

They all laughed.

'Nay,' said Muriel. 'Don't leave us all lonely, John Thomas. Take one!'

'I'll take the lot, if you like,' he responded gallantly.

'That you won't, either,' said Muriel. 'Two's company; seven's too much of a good thing.'

'Nay – take one,' said Laura. 'Fair and square, all above board, and say which.'

'Ay,' cried Annie, speaking for the first time. 'Pick, John Thomas; let's hear thee.'

'Nay,' he said. 'I'm going home quiet to-night. Feeling good, for once.'

'Whereabouts?' said Annie. 'Take a good 'un, then. But tha's got to take one of us!'

'Nay, how can I take one,' he said, laughing uneasily. 'I don't want to make enemies.'

'You'd only make *one*,' said Annie.

'The chosen *one*,' added Laura.

'Oh, my! Who said girls!' exclaimed John Thomas, again turning, as if to escape. 'Well – good-night.'

'Nay, you've got to make your pick,' said Muriel. 'Turn your face to the wall, and say which one touches you. Go on – we shall only just touch your back – one of us. Go on – turn your face to the wall, and don't look, and say which one touches you.'

He was uneasy, mistrusting them. Yet he had not the courage to break away. They pushed him to a wall and stood him there with his face to it. Behind his back they all grimaced, tittering. He looked so comical. He looked around uneasily.

'Go on!' he cried.

'You're looking – you're looking!' they shouted.

He turned his head away. And suddenly, with a movement

like a swift cat, Annie went forward and fetched him a box on the side of the head that sent his cap flying and himself staggering. He started round.

But at Annie's signal they all flew at him, slapping him, pinching him, pulling his hair, though more in fun than in spite or anger. He, however, saw red. His blue eyes flamed with strange fear as well as fury, and he butted through the girls to the door. It was locked. He wrenched at it. Roused, alert, the girls stood round and looked at him. He faced them, at bay. At that moment they were rather horrifying to him, as they stood in their short uniforms. He was distinctly afraid.

'Come on, John Thomas! Come on! Choose!' said Annie.

'What are you after? Open the door,' he said.

'We shan't – not till you've chosen!' said Muriel.

'Chosen what?' he said.

'Chosen the one you're going to marry,' she replied.

He hesitated a moment.

'Open the blasted door,' he said, 'and get back to your senses.' He spoke with official authority.

'You've got to choose!' cried the girls.

'Come on!' cried Annie, looking him in the eye. 'Come on! Come on!'

He went forward, rather vaguely. She had taken off her belt, and swinging it, she fetched him a sharp blow over the head with the buckle end. He sprang and seized her. But immediately the other girls rushed upon him, pulling and tearing and beating him. Their blood was now thoroughly up. He was their sport now. They were going to have their own back, out of him. Strange, wild creatures, they hung on him and rushed at him to bear him down. His tunic was torn right up the back, Nora had hold at the back of his collar, and was actually strangling him. Luckily the button burst. He struggled in a wild frenzy of fury and terror, almost mad terror. His tunic was simply torn off his back, his shirt-sleeves were torn away, his arms were naked. The girls rushed at him, clenched their hands on him and pulled at him: or they rushed at him and pushed him, butted him with all their might: or they struck him wild blows. He ducked and cringed and struck sideways. They became more intense.

At last he was down. They rushed on him, kneeling on him. He had neither breath nor strength to move. His face was bleeding with a long scratch, his brow was bruised.

Annie knelt on him, the other girls knelt and hung on to him. Their faces were flushed, their hair wild, their eyes glittering strangely. He lay at last quite still, with face averted, as an animal lies when it is defeated and at the mercy of the captor. Sometimes his eye glanced back at the wild faces of the girls. His breast rose heavily, his wrists were torn.

'Now, then, my fellow!' gasped Annie at length. 'Now then – now –'

At the sound of her terrifying, cold triumph, he suddenly started to struggle as an animal might, but the girls threw themselves upon him with unnatural strength and power, forcing him down.

'Yes – now, then!' gasped Annie at length.

And there was a dead silence, in which the thud of heart-beating was to be heard. It was a suspense of pure silence in every soul.

'Now you know where you are,' said Annie.

The sight of his white, bare arm maddened the girls. He lay in a kind of trance of fear and antagonism. They felt themselves filled with supernatural strength.

Suddenly Polly started to laugh – to giggle wildly – helplessly – and Emma and Muriel joined in. But Annie and Nora and Laura remained the same, tense, watchful, with gleaming eyes. He winced away from these eyes.

'Yes,' said Annie, in a curious low tone, secret and deadly. 'Yes! You've got it now! You know what you've done, don't you? You know what you've done.'

He made no sound nor sign, but lay with bright, averted eyes, and averted, bleeding face.

'You ought to be *killed*, that's what you ought,' said Annie, tensely. 'You ought to be *killed*.' And there was a terrifying lust in her voice.

Polly was ceasing to laugh, and giving long-drawn Oh-h-hs and sighs as she came to herself.

'He's got to choose,' she said vaguely.

'Oh, yes, he has,' said Laura, with vindictive decision.

'Do you hear – do you hear?' said Annie. And with a sharp movement, that made him wince, she turned his face to her.

'Do you hear?' she repeated, shaking him.

But he was quite dumb. She fetched him a sharp slap on the face. He started, and his eyes widened. Then his face darkened with defiance, after all.

'Do you hear?' she repeated.

He only looked at her with hostile eyes.

'Speak!' she said, putting her face devilishly near his.

'What?' he said, almost overcome.

'You've got to *choose*!' she cried, as if it were some terrible menace, and as if it hurt her that she could not exact more.

'What?' he said, in fear.

'Choose your girl, Coddy. You've got to choose her now. And you'll get your neck broken if you play any more of your tricks, my boy. You're settled now.'

There was a pause. Again he averted his face. He was cunning in his overthrow. He did not give in to them really – no, not if they tore him to bits.

'All right, then,' he said, 'I choose Annie.' His voice was strange and full of malice. Annie let go of him as if he had been a hot coal.

'He's chosen Annie!' said the girls in chorus.

'Me!' cried Annie. She was still kneeling, but away from him. He was still lying prostrate, with averted face. The girls grouped uneasily around.

'Me!' repeated Annie, with a terrible bitter accent.

Then she got up, drawing away from him with strange disgust and bitterness.

'I wouldn't touch him,' she said.

But her face quivered with a kind of agony, she seemed as if she would fall. The other girls turned aside. He remained lying on the floor, with his torn clothes and bleeding, averted face.

'Oh, if he's chosen –' said Polly.

'I don't want him – he can choose again,' said Annie, with the same rather bitter hopelessness.

'Get up,' said Polly, lifting his shoulder. 'Get up.'

He rose slowly, a strange, ragged, dazed creature. The girls eyed him from a distance, curiously, furtively, dangerously.

'Who wants him?' cried Laura, roughly.

'Nobody,' they answered, with contempt. Yet each one of them waited for him to look at her, hoped he would look at her. All except Annie, and something was broken in her.

He, however, kept his face closed and averted from them all. There was a silence of the end. He picked up the torn pieces of his tunic, without knowing what to do with them. The girls stood about uneasily, flushed, panting, tidying their hair and their dress unconsciously, and watching him. He looked at none of them. He espied his cap in a corner, and went and picked it up. He put it on his head, and one of the girls burst into a shrill, hysteric laugh at the sight he presented. He, however, took no heed, but went straight to where his overcoat hung on a peg. The girls moved away from contact with him as if he had been an electric wire. He put on his coat and buttoned it down. Then he rolled his tunic-rags into a bundle, and stood before the locked door, dumbly.

'Open the door, somebody,' said Laura.

'Annie's got the key,' said one.

Annie silently offered the key to the girls. Nora unlocked the door.

'Tit for tat, old man,' she said. 'Show yourself a man, and don't bear a grudge.'

But without a word or sign he had opened the door and gone, his face closed, his head dropped.

'That'll learn him,' said Laura.

'Coddy!' said Nora.

'Shut up, for God's sake!' cried Annie fiercely, as if in torture.

'Well, I'm about ready to go, Polly. Look sharp!' said Muriel.

The girls were all anxious to be off. They were tidying themselves hurriedly, with mute, stupified faces.

The Lovely Lady

At seventy-two, Pauline Attenborough could still sometimes be mistaken, in the half-light, for thirty. She really was a wonderfully preserved woman, of perfect *chic.* Of course it helps a great deal to have the right frame. She would be an exquisite skeleton, and her skull would be an exquisite skull, like that of some Etruscan woman with feminine charm still in the swerve of the bone and the pretty, naïve teeth.

Mrs Attenborough's face was of the perfect oval and slightly flat type that wears best. There is no flesh to sag. Her nose rode serenely, in its finely bridged curve. Only the big grey eyes were a tiny bit prominent, on the surface of her face, and they gave her away most. The bluish lids were heavy, as if they ached sometimes with the strain of keeping the eyes beneath them arch and bright; and at the corners of the eyes were fine little wrinkles which would slacken into haggardness, then be pulled up tense again to that bright, gay look like a Leonardo woman who really could laugh outright.

Her niece Cecilia was perhaps the only person in the world who was aware of the invisible little wire which connected Pauline's eye-wrinkles with Pauline's willpower. Only Cecilia consciously watched the eyes go haggard and old and tired, and remain so, for hours; until Robert came home. Then ping! – the mysterious little wire that worked between Pauline's will and her face went taut, the weary, haggard, prominent eyes suddenly began to gleam, the eyelids arched, the queer, curved eyebrows which floated in such frail arches on Pauline's forehead began to gather a mocking significance, and you had the *real* lovely lady, in all her charm.

She really had the secret of everlasting youth; that is to say, she could don her youth again like an eagle. But she was sparing of it. She was wise enough not to try being young for too many people. Her son Robert, in the evenings, and Sir Wilfrid Knipe sometimes in the afternoon to tea; then occasional visitors on Sunday, when Robert was home – for these she was her lovely and changeless self, that age could not wither, nor custom stale; so bright and kindly and yet subtly mocking, like Mona Lisa, who knew a thing or two. But Pauline knew more, so she needn't be smug at all. She could laugh that lovely, mocking Bacchante laugh of hers, which was at the same time never malicious, always good-naturedly tolerant, both of virtues and vices – the former, of course, taking much more tolerating. So she suggested, roguishly.

Only with her niece Cecilia she did not trouble to keep up the glamour. Ciss was not very observant, anyhow; and, more than that, she was plain; more still, she was in love with Robert; and most of all, she was thirty, and dependent on her aunt Pauline. Oh, Cecilia – why make music for her?

Cecilia, called by her aunt and by her cousin Robert just Ciss, like a cat spitting, was a big, dark-complexioned, pug-faced young woman who very rarely spoke, and when she did couldn't get it out. She was the daughter of a poor Congregational clergyman who had been, while he lived, brother to Ronald, Aunt Pauline's husband. Ronald and the Congregational minister were both well dead, and Aunt Pauline had had charge of Ciss for the last five years.

The lived all together in a quite exquisite though rather small Queen Anne house some twenty-five miles out of town, secluded in a little dale, and surrounded by small but very quaint and pleasant grounds. It was an ideal place and an ideal life for Aunt Pauline, at the age of seventy-two. When the kingfishers flashed up the little stream in her garden, going under the alders, something still flashed in her heart. She was that kind of woman.

Robert, who was two years older than Ciss, went every day to town, to his chambers in one of the Inns. He was a barrister, and, to his secret but very deep mortification, he earned about a hundred pounds a year. He simply *couldn't* get above that figure, though it was rather easy to get below it. Of course, it didn't matter. Pauline had money. But then, what was Pauline's was Pauline's, and though she could give almost lavishly, still, one was always aware of having a *lovely* and *undeserved* present made to one. Presents are so much nicer when they're undeserved, Aunt Pauline would say.

Robert, too, was plain, and almost speechless. He was medium sized, rather broad and stout, though not fat. Only his creamy, clean-shaven face was rather fat, and sometimes suggestive of an Italian priest, in its silence and its secrecy. But he had grey eyes like his mother, but very shy and uneasy, not bold like hers. Perhaps Ciss was the only person who fathomed his awful shyness and *malaise*, his habitual feeling that he was in the wrong place: almost like a soul that has got into a wrong body. But he never did anything about it. He went up to Chambers, and read law. It was, however, all the weird old processes that interested him. He had, unknown to everybody but his mother, a quite extraordinary collection of old Mexican legal documents – reports of processes and trials, pleas, accusations: the weird and awful mixture of ecclesiastical law and common law in seventeenth-century Mexico. He had started a study in this direction through coming across the report of a trial of two English sailors, for murder, in Mexico, in 1620, and he had gone on, when the next document was an accusation against a Don Miguel Estrada for seducing one of the nuns of the Sacred Heart Convent in Oaxaca in 1680.

Pauline and her son Robert had wonderful evenings with these old papers. The lovely lady knew a little Spanish. She even looked a trifle Spanish herself, with a high comb and a marvellous dark-brown shawl embroidered in thick silvery silk embroidery. So she would sit at the perfect old table, soft as velvet in its deep brown surface, a high comb in her hair, earrings with dropping pendants in her ears, her arms bare and still beautiful, a few strings of pearls round her throat, a puce velvet dress on and this or another beautiful shawl, and by candlelight she looked, yes, a Spanish high-bred beauty of thirty-two or three. She set the candles to give her face just the chiaroscuro she knew suited her; her high chair that rose behind her face was done in old green brocade, against which her face emerged like a Christmas rose.

They were always three at table, and they always drank a bottle of champagne: Pauline two glasses, Ciss two glasses, Robert the rest. The lovely lady sparkled and was radiant. Ciss, her black hair bobbed, her broad shoulders in a very nice and becoming dress that Aunt Pauline had helped her to make, stared from her aunt to her cousin and back again, with rather confused, mute hazel eyes, and played the part of an audience suitably impressed. She *was* impressed, somewhere, all the time. And even rendered speechless by Pauline's brilliancy, even after five years. But at the bottom of her consciousness was the *data* of as weird a document as Robert ever studied: all the things she knew about her aunt and her cousin.

Robert was always a gentleman, with an old-fashioned, punctilious courtesy that covered his shyness quite completely. He was, and Ciss knew it, more confused than shy. He was worse than she was. Cecilia's own confusion dated from only five years back. Robert's must have started before he was born. In the lovely lady's womb he must have felt *very* confused.

He paid all his attention to his mother, drawn to her as a humble flower to the sun. And yet, priest-like, he was all the time aware, with the tail of his consciousness, that Ciss was there, and that she was a bit shut out of it, and that something wasn't right. He was aware of the third consciousness in the room. Whereas to Pauline, her niece Cecilia was an appropriate part of her own setting, rather than a distinct consciousness.

Robert took coffee with his mother and Ciss in the warm drawing-room, where all the furniture was so lovely, all collectors' pieces – Mrs Attenborough had made her own money, dealing privately in pictures and furniture and rare things from barbaric countries – and the three talked desultorily till about eight or half-past. It was very pleasant, very cosy, very homely even; Pauline made a real home cosiness out of so much elegant material. The chat was simple, and nearly always bright. Pauline was her *real* self, emanating a friendly mockery and an odd, ironic gaiety – till there came a little pause.

At which Ciss always rose and said good-night, and carried out the coffee-tray, to prevent Burnett from intruding any more.

And then! ah, then, the lovely, glowing intimacy of the evening, between mother and son, when they deciphered manuscripts and discussed points, Pauline with that eagerness of a girl for which she was famous. And it was quite genuine. In some mysterious way she had *saved up* her power for being thrilled, in connection with a man. Robert, solid, rather quiet and subdued, seemed like the elder of the two – almost like a priest with a young girl pupil. And that was rather how he felt.

Ciss had a flat for herself just across the courtyard, over the old coach-house and stables. There were no horses. Robert kept his car in the coach-house. Ciss had three very nice rooms up there, stretching along in a row one after the other, and she had got used to the ticking of the stable clock.

But sometimes she did not go to her rooms. In the summer she would sit on the lawn, and from the open window of the drawing-room upstairs she would hear Pauline's wonderful, heart-searching laugh. And in winter the young woman would put on a thick coat and walk slowly to the little balustraded bridge over the stream, and then look back at the three lighted windows of that drawing-room where mother and son were so happy together.

Ciss loved Robert, and she believed that Pauline intended the two of them to marry – when she was dead. But poor Robert, he was so convulsed with shyness already, with man or woman. What would he be when his mother was dead? – in a dozen more years. He would be just a shell, the shell of a man who had never lived.

The strange, unspoken sympathy of the young with one another, when they are overshadowed by the old, was one of the bonds between Robert and Ciss. But another bond, which Ciss did not know how to draw tight, was the bond of passion. Poor Robert was by nature a passionate man. His silence and his agonised, though hidden, shyness were both the result of a secret physical passionateness. And how Pauline could play on this! Ah, Ciss was not blind to the eyes which he fixed on his mother – eyes fascinated yet humiliated, full of shame. He was ashamed that he was not a man. And he did not love his mother. He was fascinated by her. Completely fascinated. And for the rest, paralysed in a life-long confusion.

Ciss stayed in the garden till the lights leapt up in Pauline's bedroom – about ten o'clock. The lovely lady had retired. Robert would now stay another hour or so, alone. Then he, too, would retire. Ciss, in the dark outside, sometimes wished she could creep up to him and say: 'Oh, Robert! It's all wrong!' But Aunt Pauline would hear. And, anyhow, Ciss couldn't do it. She went off to her own rooms, once more, once more, and so for ever.

In the morning coffee was brought up on a tray to each of the rooms of the three relatives. Ciss had to be at Sir Wilfrid Knipe's at nine o'clock, to give two hours' lessons to his little grand-daughter. It was her sole serious occupation, except that she played the piano for the love of it. Robert set off to town about nine. And as a rule, Aunt Pauline appeared to lunch, though sometimes not till tea-time. When she appeared, she looked fresh and young. But she was inclined to fade rather rapidly, like a flower without water, in the daytime. Her hour was the candle hour.

So she always rested in the afternoon. When the sun shone, if possible she took a sun-bath. This was one of her secrets. Her lunch was very light; she could take her sun-and-air-bath before noon or after, as it pleased her. Often it was in the afternoon, when the sun shone very warmly into a queer little yew-walled square just behind the stables. Here Ciss stretched out the lying-chair and rugs, and put the light parasol handy in the silent little enclosure of thick dark yew-hedges beyond the old red walls of the unused stables. And hither came the lovely lady with her book. Ciss then had to be on guard in one of her own rooms, should her aunt, who was very keen-eared, hear a footstep.

One afternoon it occurred to Cecilia that she herself might while away this rather long afternoon hour by taking a sun-bath. She was growing restive. The thought of the flat roof of the stable buildings, to which she could climb from a loft at the end, started her on a new adventure. She often went on to the roof; she had to, to wind up the stable clock, which was a job she had assumed to herself. Now she took a rug, climbed out under the heavens, looked at the sky and the great elm-tops, looked at the sun, then took off her things and lay down perfectly securely, in a corner of the roof under the parapet, full in the sun.

It was rather lovely, to bask all one's length like this in warm sun and air. Yes, it was very lovely! It even seemed to melt some of the hard bitterness of her heart, some of that core of unspoken resentment which never dissolved. Luxuriously, she spread herself, so that the sun should touch her limbs fully, fully. If she had no other lover, she should have the sun! She rolled over voluptuously.

And suddenly her heart stood still in her body, and her hair almost rose on end as a voice said very softly, musingly, in her ear:

'No, Henry dear! It was not my fault you died instead of marrying that Claudia. No, darling. I was quite, quite willing for you to marry her, unsuitable though she was.'

Cecilia sank down on her rug, powerless and perspiring with dread. That awful voice, so soft, so musing, yet so unnatural. Not a human voice at all. Yet there must, there *must* be someone on the roof! Oh, how unspeakably awful!

She lifted her weak head and peeped across the sloping leads. Nobody! The chimneys were too narrow to shelter anybody. There was nobody on the roof. Then it must be someone in the trees, in the elms. Either that, or – terror unspeakable – a bodiless voice! She reared her head a little higher.

And as she did so, came the voice again:

'No, darling! I told you you would tire of her in six months. And you see it was true, dear. It was true, true, true! I wanted to spare you that. So it wasn't I who made you feel weak and disabled, wanting that very silly Claudia – poor thing, she looked so woebegone afterwards! – wanting her and not wanting her. You got yourself into that perplexity, my dear. I only warned you. What else could I do? And you lost your spirit and died without ever knowing me again. It was bitter, bitter –'

The voice faded away. Cecilia subsided weakly on to her rug, after the anguished tension of listening. Oh, it was awful. The sun shone, the sky was blue, all seemed so lovely and afternoony and summery. And yet, oh, horror! – she was going to be forced to believe in the supernatural! And she loathed the supernatural, ghosts and voices and rappings and all the rest.

But that awful, creepy, bodiless voice, with its rusty sort of whispers of an overtone! It had something so fearfully familiar in it, too! And yet was so utterly uncanny. Poor Cecilia could only lie there unclothed, and so all the more agonisingly helpless, inert, collapsed in sheer dread.

And then she heard the thing sigh! – a deep sigh that seemed weirdly familiar, yet was not human. 'Ah, well, ah well! the heart must bleed. Better it should bleed than break. It is grief, grief! But it wasn't my fault, dear. And Robert could marry our poor, dull Ciss tomorrow, if he wanted her. But he doesn't care about it, so why force him into anything?' The sounds were very uneven, sometimes only a husky sort of whisper. Listen! Listen!

Cecilia was about to give vent to loud and piercing screams of hysteria, when the last two sentences arrested her. All her caution and her cunning sprang alert. It was Aunt Pauline! It *must* be Aunt Pauline, practising ventriloquism, or something like that. What a devil she was!

Where was she? She must be lying down there, right below

where Cecilia herself was lying. And it was either some fiend's trick of ventriloquism, or else thought-transference. The sounds were very uneven; sometimes quite inaudible, sometimes only a brushing sort of noise. Ciss listened intently. No, it could not be ventriloquism. It was worse: some form of thought-transference that conveyed itself like sound. Some horror of that sort! Cecilia still lay weak and inert, too terrified to move; but she was growing calmer with suspicion. It was some diabolic trick of that unnatural woman.

But *what* a devil of a woman! She even knew that she, Cecilia, had mentally accused her of killing her son Henry. Poor Henry was Robert's elder brother, twelve years older than Robert. He had died suddenly when he was twenty-two, after an awful struggle with himself, because he was passionately in love with a young and very good-looking actress, and his mother had humorously despised him for the attachment. So he had caught some sudden ordinary disease, but the poison had gone to his brain and killed him before he ever regained consciousness. Ciss knew the few facts from her own father. And lately she had been thinking that Pauline was going to kill Robert as she had killed Henry. It was clear murder: a mother murdering her sensitive sons, who were fascinated by her: the Circe!

'I suppose I may as well get up,' murmured the dim, unbreathing voice. 'Too much sun is as bad as too little. Enough sun, enough love-thrill, enough proper food, and not too much of any of them, and a woman might live for ever. I verily believe, for ever. If she absorbs as much vitality as she expends. Or perhaps a trifle more!'

It was certainly Aunt Pauline! How – how terrible! She, Ciss, was hearing Aunt Pauline's thoughts. Oh, how ghastly! Aunt Pauline was sending out her thoughts in a sort of radio, and she, Ciss, had to *hear* what her aunt was thinking. How ghastly! How insufferable! One of them would surely have to die.

She twisted and lay inert and crumpled, staring vacantly in front of her. Vacantly! Vacantly! And her eyes were staring almost into a hole. She was staring in it unseeing, a hole going down in the corner, from the lead gutter. It meant nothing to her. Only it frightened her a little more.

When suddenly, out of the hole came a sigh and a last whisper: 'Ah well! Pauline! Get up, it's enough for to-day.' Good God! Out of the hole of the rain-pipe! The rain-pipe was acting as a speaking-tube! Impossible! No, quite possible. She had read of it even in some book. And Aunt Pauline, like the old and guilty woman she was, talked aloud to herself. That was it!

A sullen exultance sprang in Ciss's breast. *That* was why she would never have anybody, not even Robert, in her bedroom. That was why she never dozed in a chair, never sat absent-minded anywhere, but went to her room, and kept to her room, except when she roused herself to be alert. When she slackened off she talked to herself! She talked in a soft little crazy voice to herself. But she was not crazy. It was only her thoughts murmuring themselves aloud.

So she had qualms about poor Henry! Well she might have! Ciss believed that Aunt Pauline had loved her big, handsome, brilliant first-born much more than she loved Robert, and that his death had been a terrible blow and a chagrin to her. Poor Robert had been only ten years old when Henry died. Since then he had been the substitute.

Ah, how awful!

But Aunt Pauline was a strange woman. She had left her husband when Henry was a small child, some years even before Robert was born. There was no quarrel. Sometimes she saw her husband again, quite amiably, but a little mockingly. And she even gave him money.

For Pauline earned all her own. Her father had been a Consul in the East and in Naples, and a devoted collector of beautiful exotic things. When he died, soon after his grandson Henry was born, he left his collection of treasures to his daughter. And Pauline, who had really a passion and a genius for loveliness, whether in texture or form or colour, had laid the basis of her fortune on her father's collection. She had gone on collecting, buying where she could, and selling to collectors or to museums. She was one of the first to sell old, weird African figures to the museums, and ivory carvings from New Guinea. She bought Renoir as soon as she saw his pictures. But not Rousseau. And all by herself she made a fortune.

After her husband died she had not married again. She was not even *known* to have had lovers. If she did have lovers, it was not among the men who admired her most and paid her devout and open attendance. To these she was a 'friend'.

Cecilia slipped on her clothes and caught up her rug, hastening carefully down the ladder to the loft. As she descended she heard the ringing, musical call: 'All right, Ciss' – which meant that the lovely lady was finished, and returning to the house. Even her voice was wonderfully young and sonorous, beautifully balanced and self-possessed. So different from the little voice in which she talked to herself. *That* was much more the voice of an old woman.

Ciss hastened round to the yew enclosure, where lay the comfortable *chaise longue* with the various delicate rugs. Everything Pauline had was choice, to the fine straw mat on the floor. The great yew walls were beginning to cast long shadows. Only in the corner where the rugs tumbled their delicate colours was there hot, still sunshine.

The rugs folded up, the chair lifted away, Cecilia stooped to look at the mouth of the rain-pipe. There it was, in the corner, under a little hood of masonry and just projecting from the thick leaves of the creeper on the wall. If Pauline, lying there, turned her face towards the wall, she would speak into the very mouth of the tube. Cecilia was reassured. She had heard her aunt's thoughts indeed, but by no uncanny agency.

That evening, as if aware of something, Pauline was a little quieter than usual, though she looked her own serene, rather mysterious self. And after coffee she said to Robert and Ciss:

'I'm so sleepy. The sun has made me so sleepy. I feel full of sunshine like a bee. I shall go to bed, if you don't mind. You two sit and have a talk.'

Cecilia looked quickly at her cousin.

'Perhaps you'd rather be alone?' she said to him.

'No – no,' he replied. 'Do keep me company for a while, if it doesn't bore you.'

The windows were open, the scent of honeysuckle wafted in, with the sound of an owl. Robert smoked in silence. There was a sort of despair in his motionless, rather squat body. He looked like a caryatid bearing a weight.

'Do you remember Cousin Henry?' Cecilia asked him suddenly.

He looked up in surprise.

'Yes. Very well,' he said.

'What did he look like?' she said, glancing into her cousin's big, secret-troubled eyes, in which there was so much frustration.

'Oh, he was handsome: tall, and fresh-coloured, with mother's soft brown hair.' As a matter of fact, Pauline's hair was grey. 'The ladies admired him very much; and he was at all the dances.'

'And what kind of character had he?'

'Oh, very good-natured and jolly. He liked to be amused. He was rather quick and clever, like mother, and very good company.'

'And did he love your mother?'

'Very much. She loved him too – better than she does me, as a matter of fact. He was so much more nearly her idea of a man.'

'Why was he more her idea of a man?'

'Tall – handsome – attractive, and very good company – and would, I believe, have been very successful at law. I'm afraid I am merely negative in all those respects.'

Ciss looked at him attentively, with her slow-thinking hazel eyes. Under his impassive mask she knew he suffered.

'Do you think you are so much more negative than he?' she said.

He did not lift his face. But after a few moments he replied:

'My life, certainly, is a negative affair.'

She hesitated before she dared ask him:

'And do you mind?'

He did not answer her at all. Her heart sank.

'You see, I'm afraid my life is as negative as yours is,' she said. 'And I'm beginning to mind bitterly. I'm thirty.'

She saw his creamy, well-bred hand tremble.

'I suppose,' he said, without looking at her, 'one will rebel when it is too late.'

That was queer, from him.

'Robert!' she said. 'Do you like me at all?'

She saw his dusky-creamy face, so changeless in its folds, go pale.

'I am very fond of you,' he murmured.

'Won't you kiss me? Nobody ever kisses me,' she said pathetically.

He looked at her, his eyes strange with fear and a certain haughtiness. Then he rose, and came softly over to her, and kissed her gently on the cheek.

'It's an awful shame, Ciss!' he said softly.

She caught his hand and pressed it to her breast.

'And sit with me sometimes in the garden,' she said, murmuring with difficulty. 'Won't you?'

He looked at her anxiously and searchingly.

'What about mother?'

Ciss smiled a funny little smile, and looked into his eyes. He suddenly flushed crimson, turning aside his face. It was a painful sight.

'I know,' he said. 'I am no lover of women.'

He spoke with sarcastic stoicism, against himself, but even she did not know the shame it was to him.

'You never try to be,' she said.

Again his eyes changed uncannily.

'Does one have to try?' he said.

'Why, yes. One never does anything if one doesn't try.'

He went pale again.

'Perhaps you are right,' he said.

In a few minutes she left him, and went to her rooms. At least she had tried to take off the everlasting lid from things.

The weather continued sunny, Pauline continued her sunbaths, and Ciss lay on the roof eavesdropping, in the literal sense of the word. But Pauline was not to be heard. No sound came up the pipe. She must be lying with her face away into the open. Ciss listened with all her might. She could just detect the faintest, faintest murmur away below, but no audible syllable.

And at night, under the stars, Cecilia sat and waited in silence, on the seat which kept in view the drawing-room windows and the side door into the garden. She saw the light go up in her aunt's room. She saw the lights at last go out in the drawing-room. And she waited. But he did not come. She stayed on in the darkness half the night, while the owl hooted. But she stayed alone.

Two days she heard nothing; her aunt's thoughts were not revealed; and at evening nothing happened. Then, the second night, as she sat with heavy, helpless persistence in the garden, suddenly she started. He had come out. She rose and went softly over the grass to him.

'Don't speak!' he murmured.

And in silence, in the dark, they walked down the garden and over the little bridge to the paddock, where the hay, cut very late, was in cock. There they stood disconsolate under the stars.

'You see,' he said, 'how can I ask for love, if I don't feel any love in myself? You know I have a real regard for you –'

'How *can* you feel any love, when you never feel anything?' she said.

'That is true,' he replied.

And she waited for what next.

'And how can I marry?' he said. 'I am a failure even at making money. I can't ask my mother for money.'

She sighed deeply.

'Then don't bother yet about marrying,' she said. 'Only love me a little. Won't you?'

He gave a short laugh.

'It sounds so atrocious, to say it is hard to begin,' he said.

She sighed again. He was so stiff to move.

'Shall we sit down a minute?' she said. And then, as they sat on the hay, she added: 'May I touch you? Do you mind?'

'Yes, I mind. But do as you wish,' he replied, with that mixture of shyness and queer candour which made him a little ridiculous, as he knew quite well. But in his heart there was almost murder.

She touched his black, always tidy hair, with her fingers.

'I suppose I shall rebel one day,' he said again suddenly.

They sat some time, till it grew chilly. And he held her hand fast, but he never put his arms round her. At last she rose, and went indoors, saying good-night.

The next day, as Cecilia lay stunned and angry on the roof, taking her sun-bath, and becoming hot and fierce with sunshine, suddenly she started. A terror seized her in spite of herself. It was the voice.

'Caro, caro, tu non l'hai visto!' it was murmuring away, in a language Cecilia did not understand. She lay and writhed her limbs in the sun, listening intently to words she could not follow. Softly, whisperingly, with infinite caressiveness and yet with that subtle, insidious arrogance under its velvet, came the voice, murmuring in Italian: 'Bravo, si, molto bravo, poverino, ma uomo come te non sarà mai, mai, mai!' Oh, especially in Italian Cecilia heard the poisonous charm of the voice, so caressive, so soft and flexible, yet so utterly egoistic. She hated it with intensity as it sighed and whispered out of nowhere. Why, why should it be so delicate, so subtle and flexible and beautifully controlled, when she herself was so clumsy? Oh, poor Cecilia, she writhed in the afternoon sun, knowing her own clownish clumsiness and lack of suavity, in comparison.

'No, Robert dear, you will never be the man your father was, though you have some of his looks. He was a marvellous lover, soft as a flower yet piercing as a humming-bird. Cara, cara mia bellissima, ti ho aspettato come l'agonissante aspetta la morte, morte deliziosa, quasi quasi troppo deliziosa per una mera anima humana. He gave himself to a woman as he gave himself to God. Mauro! Mauro! How you loved me! How you loved me!'

The voice ceased in reverie, and Cecilia knew what she had guessed before – that Robert was not the son of her Uncle Ronald, but of some Italian.

'I am disappointed in you, Robert. There is no poignancy in you. Your father was a Jesuit, but he was the most perfect and poignant lover in the world. You are a Jesuit like a fish in a tank. And that Ciss of yours is the cat fishing for you. It is less edifying even than poor Henry.'

Cecilia suddenly bent her mouth down to the tube, and said in a deep voice:

'Leave Robert alone! Don't kill him as well.'

There was dead silence in the hot July afternoon that was lowering for thunder. Cecilia lay prostrate, her heart beating in great thumps. She was listening as if her whole soul were an ear. At last she caught the whisper:

'Did someone speak?'

She leaned again to the mouth of the tube:

'Don't kill Robert as you killed me,' she said, with slow enunciation, and a deep but small voice.

'Ah!' came the sharp little cry. 'Who is that speaking?'

'Henry,' said the deep voice.

There was dead silence. Poor Cecilia lay with all the use gone out of her. And there was dead silence. Till at last came the whisper:

'I didn't kill Henry. No, no! No, no! Henry, surely you can't blame me! I loved you, dearest; I only wanted to help you.'

'You killed me!' came the deep, artificial, accusing voice. 'Now let Robert live. Let him go! Let him marry!'

There was a pause.

'How very, very awful!' mused the whispering voice. 'Is it possible, Henry, you are a spirit, and you condemn me?'

'Yes, I condemn you!'

Cecilia felt all the pent-up rage going down that rain-pipe. At the same time, she almost laughed. It was awful.

She lay and listened and listened. No sound! As if time had ceased, she lay inert in the weakening sun, till she heard a far-off rumble of thunder. She sat up. The sky was yellowing. Quickly she dressed herself, went down, and out to the corner of the stables.

'Aunt Pauline!' she called discreetly. 'Did you hear thunder?'

'Yes, I am going in. Don't wait,' came a feeble voice.

Cecilia retired, and from the loft watched, spying, as the figure of the lovely lady, wrapped in a lovely wrap of old blue silk, went rather totteringly to the house.

The sky gradually darkened. Cecilia hastened in with the rugs. Then the storm broke. Aunt Pauline did not appear to tea. She found the thunder trying. Robert also did not arrive till after tea, in the pouring rain. Cecilia went down the covered passage to her own house, and dressed carefully for dinner, putting some white columbines at her breast.

The drawing-room was lit with a softly shaded lamp. Robert, dressed, was waiting, listening to the rain. He too seemed strangely crackling and on edge. Cecilia came in, with the white flowers nodding at her dusky breast. Robert was watching her curiously, a new look on his face. Cecilia went to the bookshelves near the door, and was peering for something, listening acutely. She heard a rustle, then the door softly opening. And as it opened, Ciss suddenly switched on the strong electric light by the door.

Her aunt, in a dress of black lace over ivory colour, stood in the doorway. Her face was made up, but haggard with a look of unspeakable irritability, as if years of suppressed exasperation and dislike of her fellow-men had suddenly crumpled her into an old witch.

'Oh, aunt!' cried Cecilia.

'Why, mother, you're a little old lady!' came the astounded voice of Robert – like an astonished boy, as if it were a joke.

'Have you only just found it out?' snapped the old woman venomously.

'Yes! Why, I thought –' his voice tailed out in misgiving.

The haggard, old Pauline, in a frenzy of exasperation, said:

'Aren't we going down?'

She had not even noticed the excess of light, a thing she shunned. And she went downstairs almost tottering.

At table she sat with her face like a crumpled mask of unspeakable irritability. She looked old, very old, and like a witch. Robert and Cecilia fetched furtive glances at her. And Ciss, watching Robert, saw that he was so astonished and repelled by his mother's looks that he was another man.

'What kind of a drive home did you have?' snapped Pauline, with an almost gibbering irritability.

'It rained, of course,' he said.

'How clever of you to have found that out!' said his mother, with the grisly grin of malice that had succeeded her arch smile.

'I don't understand,' he said, with quiet suavity.

'It's apparent,' said his mother, rapidly and sloppily eating her food.

She rushed through the meal like a crazy dog, to the utter consternation of the servant. And the moment it was over she darted in a queer, crab-like way upstairs. Robert and Cecilia followed her, thunderstruck, like two conspirators.

'You pour the coffee. I loathe it! I'm going. Good-night!' said the old woman, in a succession of sharp shots. And she scrambled out of the room.

There was a dead silence. At last he said:

'I'm afraid mother isn't well. I must persuade her to see a doctor.'

'Yes,' said Cecilia.

The evening passed in silence. Robert and Ciss stayed on in the drawing-room, having lit a fire. Outside was cold rain. Each pretended to read. They did not want to separate. The evening passed with ominous mysteriousness, yet quickly.

At about ten o'clock the door suddenly opened, and Pauline appeared, in a blue wrap. She shut the door behind her, and came to the fire. Then she looked at the two young people in hate, real hate.

'You two had better get married quickly,' she said, in an ugly voice. 'It would look more decent; such a passionate pair of lovers!'

Robert looked up at her quietly.

'I thought you believed that cousins should not marry, mother,' he said.

'I do. But you're not cousins. Your father was an Italian priest.' Pauline held her daintily slippered foot to the fire, in an old coquettish gesture. Her body tried to repeat all the old graceful gestures. But the nerve had snapped, so it was a rather dreadful caricature.

'Is that really true, mother?' he asked.

'True! What do you think? He was a distinguished man, or he wouldn't have been my lover. He was far too distinguished a man to have had you for a son. But that joy fell to me.'

'How unfortunate all round,' he said slowly.

'Unfortunate for you? *You* were lucky. It was *my* misfortune,' she said acidly to him.

She was really a dreadful sight, like a piece of lovely Venetian glass that has been dropped and gathered up again in horrible, sharp-edged fragments.

Suddenly she left the room again.

For a week it went on. She did not recover. It was as if every nerve in her body had suddenly started screaming in an insanity of discordance. The doctor came, and gave her sedatives, for she never slept. Without drugs she never slept at all, only paced back and forth in her room, looking hideous and evil, reeking with malevolence. She could not bear to see either her son or her niece. Only when either of them came she asked, in pure malice:

'Well! When's the wedding? Have you celebrated the nuptials yet?'

At first Cecilia was stunned by what she had done. She realised vaguely that her aunt, once a definite thrust of condemnation had penetrated her beautiful armour, had just collapsed, squirming, inside her shell. It was too terrible. Ciss was almost terrified into repentance. Then she thought: 'This is what she always was. Now let her live the rest of her days in her true colours.'

But Pauline would not live long. She was literally shrivelling away. She kept her room, and saw no one. She had her mirrors taken away.

Robert and Cecilia sat a good deal together. The jeering of the mad Pauline had not driven them apart, as she had hoped. But Cecilia dared not confess to him what she had done.

'Do you think your mother ever loved anybody?' Ciss asked him tentatively, rather wistfully, one evening.

He looked at her fixedly.

'Herself!' he said at last.

'She didn't even *love* herself,' said Ciss. 'It was something else. What was it?' She lifted a troubled, utterly puzzled face to him.

'Power,' he said curtly.

'But what power?' she asked. 'I don't understand.'

'Power to feed on other lives,' he said bitterly. 'She was beautiful, and she fed on life. She has fed on me as she fed on Henry. She put a sucker into one's soul, and sucked up one's essential life.'

'And don't you forgive her?'

'No.'

'Poor Aunt Pauline!'

But even Ciss did not mean it. She was only aghast.

'I *know* I've got a heart,' he said, passionately striking his breast. 'But it's almost sucked dry. I *know* I've got a soul, somewhere. But it's gnawed bare. I *hate* people who want power over others.'

Ciss was silent. What was there to say?

And two days later Pauline was found dead in her bed, having taken too much veronal, for her heart was weakened.

From the grave even she hit back at her son and her niece. She left Robert the noble sum of one thousand pounds, and Ciss one hundred. All the rest, with the nucleus of her valuable antiques, went to form the 'Pauline Attenborough Museum'.

Glossary: reading the text

The glossary gives the meanings of words as they are used in this book. Look up in a dictionary any words you are not familiar with.

A note on coins and currency

Britain's currency was decimalised in 1971. Before this the pound was divided into twenty shillings (20/- or 20s). Each shilling was divided into twelve pennies or pence (12d) and these were also divided into half-pennies (1/2d) or four quarters called farthings (1/4d). In 1971, one old shilling (1/-) was equivalent to five new pence and six-pence (6d) was two and half new pence.

- A pound coin was called a 'sovereign'
- Ten shillings was a 'half-sovereign'
- Two shillings was known as a 'florin'
- The sixpenny was called a 'tanner'

All coins that were multiples of one shilling were called 'silver', including the half-a-crown which was worth two shillings and six pence. All coins that were divisions or multiples of a penny, including the threepenny 'bit', were known as 'copper'.

In Lawrence's 1907 story ***A Prelude***, Fred, a farm labourer, earns under £3 a year.

Adolf

1 ***peewits*** wading birds, also known as lapwings.

1 ***morsel*** a small piece.

1 ***enigmatically*** in a puzzling way.

3 ***circumvented*** avoided.

3 ***asphyxiated*** death by lack of oxygen.

3 ***parlour*** the best room or lounge.

4 ***palpitated*** quivered or trembled.

4 ***wantonness*** foolishness and cruelty.

4 ***scullery*** a small work room.

4 ***askance*** with a sideways look.

4 ***'Back your life it is'*** 'Of course it is' or 'Bet your life it is' (a Nottinghamshire saying).

5 ***hind-quarters*** the back end of an animal including legs and rump.

5 ***pensively*** thoughtfully.

6 ***ebullition*** outburst.

6 ***abstract meditation*** vague thoughts.

7 ***nebulous*** unclear or vague.

7 ***coppice*** a small wood.

7 ***rend*** to tear or rip.

7 ***cajoling*** persuading.

1. What is your impression of the father as the story starts?
2. Why is the mother so against the rabbit? Does her view change later?
3. How does the rabbit behave once it has got used to the family?
4. Do you think the narrator felt the rabbit was better off in its natural environment?

Rex

9 ***flirty*** flirtatious.

9 ***dog-cart*** a small horse-drawn vehicle.

9 ***Band of Hope*** a society for children which was against the drinking of alcohol.

9 ***éclat*** showy splendour (French).

9 ***palatial*** like a palace.

10 **Rex** king (Latin).

10 ***naïveté*** simpleness (French).

11 **infra dig** undignified – short for *infra dignitatem* 'beneath one's dignity' (Latin).

11 ***fastidious*** difficult to please.

11 ***'Wag thy strunt, then!'*** 'Wag your tail'.

11 ***toused*** tore at.

11 ***interpolated*** introduced as an alternative view.

12 ***vociferously*** strongly and loudly.

12 ***expostulated*** tried to reason.

12 **in flagrante** in the act (Latin).

13 **comme il faut** correct (French).

13 ***rapine*** plunder.

14 **besoin d'aimer** need to love (French).

14 ***supervening*** coming closely after.

14 ***paroxysms*** fits.

16 ***staccato*** short and abrupt (Italian).

16 **suffisance** conceit (French).

16 ***ostentatiously*** showing off.

17 ***mard-soft*** coddling or pampering (a dialect word).

1 What is it that makes the mother and Rex such enemies?
2 Why is Rex so loving and yet so wild?
3 Was the uncle right to accuse the children of spoiling the little dog? What did he mean?

A Prelude

19 ***'Sweet is pleasure after pain . . .'*** from *Alexander's Feast* by John Dryden (1631–1700).

20 ***assented*** agreed.

20 ***'at the pit . . .'*** mining was much better paid than other working-class jobs but the risk of death or injury was very high.

21 ***dues*** rewards.

22 ***'We shall not do . . .'*** 'We are not good enough'.

22 ***irrepressible*** stubborn.

22 ***guysers*** this is a traditional and local name for the young men who dressed up with masks and fancy dress at Christmas and then performed a play or mime about St George set in the Middle East (they were also called mummers).

23 ***a gathered face*** face covered with sores or spots.

23 ***Beelzebub*** the Devil.

23 ***a hurricane lamp*** an oil lamp in a case to protect the flame in strong winds.

24 ***Bedouins*** nomadic Arabs.

24 ***bucolic*** rustic or rural and idyllic.

24 ***burnouse*** a cloak with a hood worn by Arabs.

25 ***squab*** a soft couch.

25 ***ingle-nook*** a fire-side corner.

26 ***metamorphosed*** changed or transformed.

27 ***consternation*** sudden confusion.

28 ***paternal*** concerned and fatherly.

28 ***slough*** wet muddy ground.

30 ***Giordani's*** Giuseppe Giordani was an eighteenth-century song writer.

1. What is the mother brooding over at Christmas? How does her mood change?
2. How does the Christmas play show how awkward things have become between Fred and Nellie?
3. What has happened to divide the lovers?

Lessford's Rabbits

31 ***disposition*** a person's natural way of acting.

32 ***ratification*** approval and agreement.

33 ***squalling*** quarrelling loudly.

35 ***I hung fire*** I waited a bit.

36 ***debonair*** cheerful, with good manners.

36 ***inveterate*** habitual.

36 ***mercurial*** changeable and fitful.

37 ***ironical*** mocking.

38 ***Empire*** a name of a cinema.

1. What is the narrator's (Lawrence's) mood at the start of the tale?
2. How does the image of the pleasure boat (page 32) explain how the narrator felt when the Infant mistress was helping with breakfast?
3. Do you think he is really annoyed with the boys at the end?

A Lesson on a Tortoise

39 ***spent*** drained and exhausted.

39 ***bade*** asked.

39 ***London Home boys*** lads from a home for disobedient boys.

40 ***covertly*** secretively.

40 ***diligently*** carefully and actively.

41 ***lacquer*** a varnish.

41 ***plaintive*** sad.

41 ***monitor*** the boy responsible for the classroom materials.

42 ***impudent indignation*** bold and rude anger.

43 ***deferential*** respectful.

1. What is the mood of the teacher and the pupils at the start of the lesson? Who is the narrator of this tale?
2. Why is the teacher confused and angered by the stealing going on in the class?
3. Why in your own view is the teacher so sad at the end of the tale?

The Shades of Spring

45 ***diapered with woodruff*** patterned with woodruff – a shrub with white flowers.

45 ***dog-mercury*** a small green plant with catkins.

45 ***hyacinth*** a small plant with blue, bell-like flowers.

46 ***nettled*** irritated.

48 ***azure*** a clear, sky-blue colour.

50 ***pipkin*** a deep bowl used for cooking.

50 *'You call it lunch, don't you?'* middle-class people tended to call the midday meal 'lunch' rather than the more working-class 'dinner'.

52 *fervently* enthusiastically.

52 *long-shanked . . . scissors* scissors that have a long part between the metal loops and the joint.

53 *sycock* a local word for a thrush.

53 *throstle . . . blackie* dialect for song thrush and blackbird.

54 *Arcady* Arcadia, the ideal rural region found in literature.

55 *pennons* long narrow flags.

59 *'Qu'il était ... l'espoir'* 'How blue was the sky, and high the hope' – a line from a poem 'Colloque sentimental' (A sentimental conversation) by Paul Verlaine (1844–96). The next line is: 'Hope has fled, vanquished, towards the black sky.'

59 *his Botticelli angel* Botticelli was an Italian artist (*c.* 1445–1510). The people in his paintings are often very beautiful but don't look like real human beings.

59 *Beatrice* The Italian poet Dante (1265–1321) fell in love with a girl whom he called Beatrice and wrote many poems about her. He idealised her but she married someone else and died young.

60 *William Morris* (1834–96) an English artist, writer, craftsman and socialist who was fascinated by the Middle Ages and Arthurian legends.

1. How does Syson react to the interruption of Arthur the gamekeeper as he visits his old haunts?
2. What do the words 'lunch' and 'dinner' tell us about the social positions of Syson and Hilda?
3. Why does Hilda finally reject Syson and what attracts her to Arthur?

Second Best

63 ***petulantly*** in a bad temper.

63 ***whimsical*** changeable, constantly having different ideas.

63 ***spasmodic*** erratic, emotional.

64 ***Ollerton*** a town about twelve miles north of Nottingham with two feast or fair days, one on 1 May and the other on 26 September.

65 ***'fret her fat'*** worry or 'wear away her fat' (local dialect).

65 ***sere*** withered and dried up.

65 **joie de vivre** joy of life (French).

68 ***harebells*** small flowers like bluebells.

69 ***tresses*** leafy shoots (usually locks or plaits of hair).

69 ***poignantly*** bitterly.

70 ***moudiwarp*** local dialect for a mole.

70 ***'got your rag out'*** 'made you very angry'.

70 ***an admonitory pat*** a warning pat.

72 ***winsome*** charming and attractive.

1. In what ways are the characters of the two sisters different?
2. How do you think the blindness of the mole compares with the blindness or confusion of the humans in the story?
3. In what ways are Jimmy and Tom different from each other?
4. Why do you think that Frances finally accepts the attentions of Tom?

Her Turn

73 ***prudery*** modesty or primness.

73 ***naïve*** simple.

73 ***strike-pay*** if the miner was a member of the union he was entitled to 10/- per week, plus 1/- for each child under 13 years old.

73 ***second strike*** there was a strike in Lawrence's town of Eastwood in 1910 and then a national coal strike in 1912.

74 **conundrums** puzzles.

75 ***'I'd rather ha'e a smite o' cheese ...'*** 'I would rather have a bit of cheese ...'.

76 ***tan-tafflins*** a small cake (Nottinghamshire dialect).

76 ***'strap'*** credit.

77 **desultory** random or erratic.

77 ***'He's wakkened up betimes'*** 'He has woken up early'.

78 **corker** something really good.

78 ***'this is a winder!'*** 'this takes my breath away'.

1 What sort of relationship do Mr and Mrs Radford have? What phrases suggest how they get on?
2 How does the little poem Radford writes suggest what happens between them?
3 At the end of the story, why does Radford go to the tortoise and why is Mrs Radford compared to a cat?

Tickets, Please

80 ***the county town*** this was modelled on Nottingham.

81 ***hussies*** badly behaved women.

81 sang-froid self-composure, coolness (French).

81 *antiphony* an echoing or alternating sound as in some church music.

82 *peremptory* commanding, dictatorial.

82 *Thermopylae* a narrow pass where the Greeks in 480 BC fought to the death to try to prevent the Persian army from entering Greece.

82 *Coddy* slang word for penis (as is 'John Thomas').

83 *comely* attractive.

83 *Tartar* a quarrelsome, ill-tempered person (the Tartars were a people of Central Asia who, led by Genghis Khan, conquered much of Asia and Eastern Europe in the Middle Ages).

83 *cock-of-the walk* dominant bully, chief ruler.

83 *Statutes fair* an annual fair held in many towns, legalised by statute. It was also held in Lawrence's own town, Eastwood.

84 *naphtha* oil for lights or heaters.

84 *complaisant* accommodating, agreeable.

84 *quoits* iron or wooden rings.

85 *nonchalantly* coolly and unconcerned.

87 *on the qui-vive* alert, on the look out (French).

94 *stupified* (usually stupefied) stunned, dazed.

1. What sort of character is Annie? How is she attracted to John Thomas?
2. What makes John Thomas reject Annie?
3. Do you think that the tram women were justified in their treatment of John Thomas?
4. Can you explain the writer's view of John Thomas? Is the narrator (Lawrence) at all sympathetic towards him?

The Lovely Lady

95 ***Etruscan*** an ancient people from Italy; Lawrence was fascinated by their tomb paintings.

95 ***serenely*** calmly and sedately.

95 ***Leonardo woman*** a reference to the *Mona Lisa* by the Italian painter Leonardo da Vinci (1452–1519). The woman in the portrait looks amused but does not laugh outright.

96 ***age could not wither, nor custom stale*** a quotation from Shakespeare's *Antony and Cleopatra* (Act 2, scene 2) describing the beautiful Queen of Egypt.

96 ***Bacchante*** a drunken and riotous female follower of Bacchus, the Greek and Roman god of wine and ecstasy.

96 ***Congregational*** a member of a Protestant Church that dates from the sixteenth century.

97 **malaise** sickness, boredom.

98 ***punctilious*** careful, strictly observant.

98 ***desultorily*** jumping from one subject to another.

99 ***emanating*** making arise.

99 ***balustraded*** railed, banistered.

103 ***Circe*** the mythical Greek enchantress who turned the companions of Ulysses (Odysseus) into pigs.

104 ***exultance*** delight, triumph.

105 **Renoir** and **Rousseau** two famous French painters (1841–1919 and 1844–1910).

105 **chaise longue** a couch (French).

106 ***caryatid*** a female figure sculptured as a column.

107 ***stoicism*** repression of emotion.

109 ***'Caro ... l'hai visto!'*** 'Dear man, dear man, you did not see him!' (Italian).

109 ***insidious*** sly, treacherous.

109 ***'Bravo . . . mai, mai!'*** 'Good, yes, very good, poor little man, but a man like you, he will never ever be!' (Italian).

109 ***suavity*** smoothness.

110 ***'Cara . . . anima humana'*** 'Dear woman, my most beautiful woman, I have waited for you like one in agony waits for death, delicious death, almost too delightful for a mere human soul' (Italian).

114 ***nuptials*** the marriage ceremony.

1. What sort of woman is Mrs Attenborough?
2. How was Robert controlled by his mother? Why was Henry so much better?
3. In your view was Ciss right to frighten Mrs Attenborough so she could have Robert?
4. Why was Ciss so shocked by what happened to Mrs Attenborough?

Study programme

The following activities are designed to encourage you to get more out of the stories and help you respond to them from a critical and personal point of view. They will help you prepare for the 'Study questions' on page 139.

Note to the reader: comparing the stories

Lawrence's writing is full of his own ideas about life. These concerns and themes work skilfully together in the stories. The list below shows where you can compare Lawrence's themes. The major themes are:

(A) Animals and nature
(B) Family and mothers
(C) Men, women and relationships
(D) Social class and status
(E) The human spirit
(F) Compulsion and destiny.

Adolf	A	B				
Rex	A	B			E	
A Prelude		B	C	D		
Lessford's Rabbits	A			D	E	
A Lesson on a Tortoise	A			D	E	
The Shades of Spring	A	B	C	D	E	F
Second Best	A		C	D	E	F
Her Turn	A	B	C		E	
Tickets, Please			C		E	F
The Lovely Lady		B	C	D	E	F

After most stories or pairs of stories there are ideas for comparing the stories. These are marked **C**.

Adolf

1 Re-read the first few paragraphs and write a brief description of the father's appearance and personality. Think carefully about the phrase, 'He liked non-human things best' and what it really tells you about him. In contrast, the mother's attitude to the new pet is hostile. Jot down the objections and opposing remarks she makes when the rabbit is first in the house.

In role, perform a short discussion the parents might have had once the children have gone to bed. Try to show the real tension between them and why the father was a 'disturbing presence' in the family and why the mother was so abrupt.

2 This autobiographical sketch recalls a childhood memory of Lawrence. The young boy is a character in his own story. How do you get to know what Lawrence thinks of the rabbit? Pick out five phrases in the story which you think show what the narrator feels about the new pet.

3 The rabbit is young but it is wild. Discuss how you look after a domestic rabbit and then look back at the text to pick out things in Adolf's behaviour which suggest that he would never be tamed.

4 Next to your list of Adolf's behaviour jot down the words that hint at the excitement of the children and the cuteness of the rabbit. Can you remember the excitement of your first pet? Thinking carefully of the words and phrases that could describe your feelings at that time, write a short story of your experience.

Rex

1 After the 'messing' episode, the mother exclaims about Rex to the children, 'you've undone all the good it would do him, with your soft ways'. What does she mean?

2 Consider how the children describe the dog and then contrast this with some of the adult descriptions of his behaviour. Which are more suitable descriptions of Rex?

3 Lawrence describes the dog in ***Rex*** as a 'fat, animated little teacup' – what does he mean? Search out some other information or description that indicates the narrator's view of the dog. Is the young Lawrence really sure he likes the dog?

C 4 ***Adolf*** and ***Rex*** are companion tales. In both, the children are excited about the pets. Father and Mother have different attitudes to Rex. In one column jot down the things Rex does, and in another column select quotes to show the reaction of the parents. Then do the same for Adolf.

What is the difference between the parents' attitudes and reactions to the misdemeanours of the two animals?

C 5 In ***Adolf*** and ***Rex*** Lawrence appears charmed by the ways of the two animals, but he also suggests that the wildness cannot be tamed. Jot down ideas from the two stories and your own views about the pros and cons of keeping wild animals.

C 6 Take a careful look at the last few paragraphs in both ***Adolf*** and ***Rex***. Which phrases explain the feelings of the children? Why did the wildness of the creatures overcome the 'love' of the children?

A Prelude

1. ***A Prelude*** is a tale which has plenty of rural detail. Read the description of the kitchen at the start of the story. Note down the words which give you details of the room and people in it. What do your notes suggest about the life of the family?

2. Lawrence's descriptions of people are often very detailed and the look of a person can suggest his/her personality. The brothers in this story are finely drawn. Sketch the brothers, labelling their appearance and personalities. Brainstorm some words to describe them. How do their descriptions match their behaviour in the story?

3. The story starts slowly and builds up with description of the characters and places. Using a timeline, look at the different episodes in the plot. Note on top of the timeline what happens to the characters while below note the setting and the mood of the tale. For example:

Mother preparing food.	. . .	The lads come in to eat supper.
The kitchen. The mother seems concerned.	. . .	They get excited about the idea of guysering.

   What are the most decisive points in this tale of love and how does Lawrence describe the mood of these episodes?

4. Lawrence disliked the idea of social class and the class system. ***A Prelude*** shows status getting in the way of true love. What do Fred and Nellie say about the way money and class have come between them? What does the last line suggest about love and status?

Lessford's Rabbits

1 For this story from his time as a teacher, Lawrence uses the first-person narrative. Note down the phrases in the tale which suggest that the rooms or the routine he is going through are forbidding, rigid and ordered. Would you say that he enjoyed the breakfast duty?

As a role-play, take the part of Lawrence and describe how he runs the periods when free breakfasts are given out. Explain his feelings about his responsibilities and what goes on.

2 The two boys, Lessford and Halket, seem to be opposites. Lessford is described as looking 'furtively' and Halket as 'debonair'. Compare the two of them by writing down all the details Lawrence gives for each one. Which do you think is the wilder and more defiant of the two?

3 The story does not really seem to have an ending: it is open-ended. Explain what you think has happened to the rabbits.

4 Even though the story is written in the first person Lawrence does not explain what he thinks of the boys at the end – he leaves it to you to think over what they have done. Compile your evidence from the story and explain in a statement what Lawrence's opinion of these two needy boys really is. Does he admire them?

C 5 Look at both ***A Lesson on a Tortoise*** and ***Lessford's Rabbits*** and discuss the different ways the school children behave in class and their attitude to school. Is school a positive and enjoyable experience? Jot down the phrases from both stories that explain Lawrence's disillusionment with school and his experience as a teacher. Which phrase best sums up his feelings about the children and school?

A Lesson on a Tortoise

1 The tale was written while Lawrence was a teacher. It is autobiographical and shows his deep frustration with his work. Pick out some sentences that show how Lawrence's mood changes as the lesson progresses.

2 Write a letter as if you were Lawrence writing to his mother in Nottingham. Imagine the tortoise lesson is the last straw, and you are going to give up the job. Using your own and Lawrence's words, describe what happened and explain your reasons for leaving and how you have lost your spirit for teaching.

3 The reptile is calm through most of this tale, but in comparison the boys and the teacher are a bit 'untamed' and upset. You know Lawrence's thoughts. Write a script explaining what the Gordons or the actors might say after the lesson. Include: their excitement about the tortoise; what they say about the teacher; and what has happened – would they blame each other?

4 The tortoise is unworried until the confusion in the classroom gets too much. Which phrase tells us that he can stand it no more? Write Joe's thoughts in a thought bubble after he withdraws into his shell. What has he seen and who is wild now?

Look back to ***Rex***. Write some similar thought bubbles from Rex's point of view. Does he think he has been spoilt and why does he behave so badly?

The Shades of Spring

1 At the beginning of the tale, Syson was an 'uneasy spirit' but thought the countryside was unchanged. Jot down any other

references to spirit you can see as the tale progresses. Look closely at the behaviour and conversation between Hilda and him. Identify what you see as the differences between them and explain why she declares to Syson, 'I disapprove of what you have become' (page 57) but describes herself as 'I am like a plant' (page 55). Whose spirit is stronger?

2 Look at the brief passage describing Hilda and Syson together which starts, 'Hilda was very womanly …' (page 51). Make a note of any other passages or dialogue in the tale that hint at their past, their attraction and her strength. Using examples, explain the intensity and balance of power between them.

After reading the last couple of pages of the story, add what Arthur has got that Syson lacks and why Hilda makes a positive decision about her fate.

C 3 One of the most individual features of Lawrence's writing is his use of detailed sketches and setting to create mood. Lawrence's love of Nature and the rural landscape comes across very strongly in ***The Shades of Spring*** and ***A Prelude***.

Note down, with a spidergram headed 'The Countryside', the fine descriptions of the landscape in both stories. Write a detailed explanation of the mood the outdoor descriptions create in both stories, and explain why the countryside is so important to the main characters.

Second Best

1 Lawrence chooses his images very carefully to emphasise atmosphere, ideas and symbolism. This tale is about the blind search for love. As you re-read the story note down all the passages describing:

- the landscape and mood

- the feelings of Frances
- the appearance and action of the mole

How does the movement and look of the mole match the morning's mood and the temperament of Frances? Later she kills a sightless, 'fumbling' mole and takes it to Tom. How does this symbolise the end of her love for Jimmy?

2 In this tale neither of the men is quite suitable in Frances' eyes. Compile a statement bank about each of the people in the love triangle: Frances, Jimmy and Tom. Note down:

– who they are
– where they are
– what they are doing
– what they are like.

Can you sympathise or empathise with Frances?

Write a letter from Frances to Jimmy disclosing all her feelings about what Jimmy has done and why she has 'chosen' Tom. Show her confusion and discontent.

C 3 In ***Second Best*** and ***The Shades of Spring*** the women have to make choices. Draw up a grid showing links between the countryside and the feelings of the characters in these two stories. Are there any connections or similarities between Lawrence's descriptions and the feelings of the characters in both stories?

Her Turn

1 This tale, written during the 1912 National Coal Miners' Strike, is also about a struggle between a man and a woman. What does the first sentence of the story suggest about their relationship? Find some phrases that sum up Mrs Radford's feelings about her husband and resentment of the situation.

What indications are there that she is deeply attracted to him? Plot a graph showing the individual peaks and troughs of their conflict.

2 Lawrence often gives the reader clues about the personality of his characters in his descriptions. Look at the descriptions of Radford (page 73) and Mrs Radford (page 75). Lawrence has chosen his words very carefully, so what do they tell you about the temperament of the two?

3 Write a film or TV script for the scenes in the story after Radford comes home from the pub. Using the description and dialogue of the story try to create the mood and tension of the scenes. Remember the details of the husband and wife and the mining background to the confrontation.

How does Lawrence give you clues to the way they are thinking, behaving and saying their dialogue? What does the way the two speak and the words they use tell you about their personalities?

4 Using a timeline, note down, as the story develops, who has the power in this relationship between husband and wife. When do you start to think that the wife may be in control? How does the tale keep you in suspense and guessing what the outcome of the conflict might be?

C 5 In ***Her Turn*** and ***Adolf*** the husband and wife have conflicting ideas. Jot down the different attitudes to life and marriage that the two men and two women have in the stories. How does the behaviour of the couples compare? Is the tension between the couples in any way similar?

Tickets, Please

1 In ***Tickets, Please*** Lawrence returns to his Nottingham background and explores a conflict with the women taking revenge on an arrogant man. The power of touch and sensual body contact are at the core of the attraction between John Thomas and Annie. Carefully re-read the story, especially the episode in the show-ground and at the end when Annie and the girls confront John Thomas.

At first what really excites Annie and how does he tease her? What happens to Annie in the waiting-room? How do her feelings change? Look at 'But her face quivered with a kind of agony' and 'something was broken in her'. Does she hate him at the end?

2 In this tale, the women are outraged at the promiscuous John Thomas and so take their revenge, but who wins the battle?

Imagine that John Thomas is asked to explain to his boss what happened with the women and the reasons and circumstances behind the disorder that night. Role-play the interview.

3 Now role-play an interview between Annie and her boss on the same subject. How much would she tell?

After the interview, Annie writes to her best friend who is doing war service on a farm outside Nottingham. She tells her what she really feels, explains what really happened and how men and women might treat each other in the future. Compose this letter.

4 Write two diary records of what Nellie in ***A Prelude*** and Annie in ***Tickets, Please*** might be thinking during these stories. You might write down in three or four entries all their thoughts about the situation and what happens, their social and work positions, their sexual attraction to the men, and the very different outcomes to the stories.

The Lovely Lady

1 Mrs Attenborough appears to be a strong old lady at the start of the story – list some phrases that suggest her strength and looks. Then, next to your first list jot down some of the ways Ciss knows the 'lovely lady' is weak and old. Lastly, in a third column note down the weaknesses of Robert and his closeness to his mother.

Do you think that the details of the old lady and the son are realistic? Is their relationship a healthy one? What do the descriptions hint about their personalities?

Using your notes, discuss how these descriptions suggest what is going to happen in the story.

2 In this story, Ciss is left in little doubt that Mrs Attenborough does not see her as a suitable daughter-in-law. Note down all the phrases that show the position of Ciss in the family. In your view what are Mrs Attenborough's objections to Ciss? Remember to look at all the details you are given about Ciss, including her looks.

3 The 'lovely lady' is taken in by Cecilia's voice down the rain-pipe (pages 110–11). Note down what Mrs Attenborough might have on her conscience. Write down some of the dreams Mrs Attenborough might have while she is asleep in her room. Think about:

- what she says in her daydreams
- how she might think of Ciss
- her memories of the past and her first son
- what she thinks of her second son
- what she thinks of the ghostly voice

Is the dream a nightmare and does it show what the 'lovely lady' is really like?

4 Ciss feels a strange compulsion to torment Mrs Attenborough. Discuss whether she has good reasons to play her ghostly trick. The spirit of Mrs Attenborough appears to be broken at the end. What physical evidence does Lawrence give you of the 'lovely lady's' defeat?

5 Ciss takes control of her destiny in ***The Lovely Lady*** but she is shocked by the decline of Mrs Attenborough. Near the end, Robert says, 'I *hate* people who want power over others.' Why do you think Ciss did not tell him what she had done? What difference does the twist at the end make to the game of power between the three characters? Which character in the story do you prefer? Explain your reasons.

6 ***The Shades of Spring*** and ***The Lovely Lady*** are about strong-willed women who get their man. If they were to meet, describe in a dialogue what they would have in common in their struggle to find love. What would they agree and disagree on when talking about 'getting their man'?

7 Look back at ***A Prelude***. Discuss how similar Fred's and Nellie's views and experience of the problems of social class are to Ciss's experience in ***The Lovely Lady***.

Study questions: comparing the stories

Many of the activities you have already completed will help you to answer the following questions. Before you begin to write, consider the following points about essay writing.

- Analyse what the question is asking. Do this by circling key words or phrases and numbering each part.
- Use each part of the question to 'brainstorm' ideas and references to the story which you think are relevant to the answer.
- Decide on the order in which you are going to tackle the parts of

the question. It may help you to draw a flow-diagram of the parts so that you can see which aspects of the question are linked.

- Organise your ideas and quotations into sections to fit your flow diagram. You can do this by placing notes in columns under relevant headings.
- Write a first draft of your essay. Do not concern yourself too much with paragraphing; just aim to get your ideas down on paper and do not be too critical of what you write.
- Redraft as many times as you need, ensuring all the time that
  - each paragraph addresses the question
  - each paragraph addresses a new part of the question, or at lest develops a part
  - you have an opening and closing paragraph which are clear and linked to the question set
  - you have checked for spelling and grammatical errors.

1 ***Adolf*** and ***Rex*** are written in the first person. Explain how this technique helps the reader into Lawrence's world and shows you his feelings and concerns.

2 Explain how ***Lessford's Rabbits*** and ***A Lesson on a Tortoise*** reveal Lawrence's personal feelings and experiences as a teacher.

3 Describe the animals in two or three of the stories. Compare them, and explain what makes them different from and similar to the humans in the tales.

4 Choose two or three stories and write about the way Lawrence shows family relationships. Give the basic features of the families in your chosen stories and explain how Lawrence uses language and the structure of the tales to explore his ideas.

5 The struggle for love between men and women is a major

theme in Lawrence's fiction. For him there is an underlying current of confusion between the sexes. Explain, with examples, whether Lawrence sympathises with women or men. Who are stronger, his male or female characters?

6 Lawrence often uses detailed description to hint at the personality of his characters or to create mood and atmosphere in his tales. With your knowledge of the tales, analyse this very particular use of language.

7 The couples in Lawrence's tales are often confused by their emotions and feelings. Compare the way two or more couples seem to be compulsively attracted to each other. Try to pick couples who stay together and those who split up.

8 In some of the stories in this collection, the characters make positive choices about their lives. Using examples, discuss how Lawrence's characters get what they want.

9 Lawrence said, 'Never trust the story-teller, trust the tale.' Reflecting on two or three tales, compare your reactions to a few characters and their situations. Who do you think acts properly in a difficult situation? Who can you sympathise with and why? Who is utterly dislikeable and why?

Suggestions for further reading

Books by D H Lawrence

Sons and Lovers
This autobiographical novel gives an insight into Lawrence's early life in Nottingham.

Some of his novellas – ***St Mawr***, ***The Fox*** and ***The Captain's Doll*** – are interesting to compare with the short stories.

The plays, ***The Widowing of Mrs Holroyd***, ***A Collier's Friday Night*** and ***The Daughter-in-Law*** explore family relationships in a way that casts a useful comparative light on many of the tales in this collection.

Short story collections by other writers

Katherine Mansfield was born about the same time as D H Lawrence. She writes in her short stories about growing up in New Zealand at the end of the nineteenth century and her later travels around Europe. Her ***Selected Stories*** would make good comparative reading, especially tales like ***Her First Ball*** or ***Daughters of the Late Colonel***.

The ***Wessex Tales*** by Thomas Hardy (Addison Wesley Longman) has some fine stories of rural life and country descriptions from the second half of the nineteenth century. ***The Withered Arm*** and ***Old Mrs Chundle*** are particularly good for looking at relationships, setting and class.

Bernard Mac Laverty writes about growing up in Northern Ireland in the 1950s and is a very fine modern author of short stories. *The Bernard Mac Laverty Collection* (Addison Wesley Longman) has some powerful stories based around the family such as ***Father and Son*** and ***A Time to Dance***.

Summer Lightning by Olive Senior (Addison Wesley Longman) and ***The Selected Stories*** by Nadine Gordimer (Penguin), contain interesting accounts of growing up in the Caribbean and Africa.

Green Behind the Grass by Adèle Geras is an attractive collection of love stories to compare with Lawrence's tales.

Wider reading assignments

1. Compare and contrast D H Lawrence's writing style and themes with another author of short stories.

2 Using examples from this collection and from other short stories you have read, explain how growing up and relationships are different today from in Lawrence's time.

3 The short story often tries to capture the 'heart' of a situation. Using two examples you have read, explain how they tell a story quickly and successfully.

4 Select two short stories you have read and describe the way the language of the authors helps tell the tale and keep the interest of the reader.

5 Examine the settings of two or three short stories by different writers. How are the mood and characters in the stories affected by the scenery in the tale?

6 Choose two or three stories with similar plots and themes. Describe how the characters face their circumstances and then deal with them.

Classic Longman Literature

Fiction

Jane Austen ***Pride and Prejudice*** 0 582 07720 6
Charlotte Brontë ***Jane Eyre*** 0 582 07719 2
Charles Dickens ***Great Expectations*** 0 582 07783 4
Oliver Twist 0 582 28729 4
George Eliot ***Silas Marner*** 0 582 23662 2
Thomas Hardy ***The Mayor of Casterbridge*** 0 582 22586 8

Collections

Characters from Pre-20th Century Novels selected by Susie Cambell 0 582 25388 8
Diaries and Letters selected by Celeste Flower 0 582 25384 5
Highlights from 19th-Century Novels selected by Linda Marsh 0 582 25385 3
Landmarks selected by Linda Marsh 0 582 25389 6
Mystery and Horror selected by Celeste Flower 0 582 28928 9
Nineteenth-Century Short Stories of Passion and Mystery selected by Tony Parkinson 0 582 33807 7
Stories Old and New selected by Geoff Barton 0 582 28931 9
Travel Writing selected by Linda Marsh 0 582 25386 1
Twisters: stories from other centuries various writers 0 582 29253 0
Two Centuries selected by Geoff Barton 0 582 25390 X
War Stories selected by Jane Christopher 0 582 28927 0
The Wessex Tales Thomas Hardy 0 582 25405 1

Plays

Charles Dickens ***A Christmas Carol*** 0 582 23664 9
Oliver Goldsmith ***She Stoops to Conquer*** 0 582 25397 7
Henrik Ibsen ***Three Plays: A Doll's House, Ghosts, The Wild Duck*** 0 582 24948 1
Christopher Marlowe ***Doctor Faustus*** 0 582 25409 4
Bernard Shaw ***Arms and the Man*** 0 582 07785 0
The Devil's Disciple 0 582 25410 8
John Webster ***The Duchess of Malfi*** 0 582 28731 6
Oscar Wilde ***The Importance of Being Earnest*** 0 582 07784 2

Poetry

Poems from Other Centuries edited by Adrian Tissier 0 582 22585 X